MODERN ESSENTIALS™

Living

AROMA
TOOLS™

PUBLISHED AND DISTRIBUTED:
AromaTools™
439 S. Pleasant Grove Blvd.
Pleasant Grove, UT 84062
Phone: 1-866-728-0070 • 801-798-7921
Internet: www.AromaTools.com
E-mail: Publications@AromaTools.com

ISBN NUMBER:
978-1-937702-40-3

DISCLAIMER:
This book has been designed to provide
information to help educate the reader in regard
to the subject matter covered. It is sold with the
understanding that the publisher and the authors are
not liable for the misconception and misuse of the
information provided. It is not provided in order
to diagnose, proscribe, or treat any disease, illness,
or injured condition of the body. The authors and
publisher shall have neither liability nor responsibility
to any person or entity with respect to any
loss, damage, or injury caused, or alleged to be
caused, directly or indirectly by the information
contained in this book. The information presented
herein is in no way intended as a substitute for
medical counseling. Anyone suffering from any
disease, illness, or injury should consult a
qualified health care professional.

Printed and bound in the U.S.A.

TABLE OF CONTENTS

An Introduction to Essential Oils

Essential oils are produced by plants and can be experienced in nature when you stroll through a garden enveloped with the scent of roses or step on a peppermint plant. Aromatic plants produce essential oils that are both volatile (they evaporate) and oil soluble (they easily mix with oils and fats), contributing to the fragrant smells we associate with certain plants.

Since the beginning of early civilization, aromatic plants have been used for their therapeutic properties. Specifically, essential oils can be used to support healthy body system functioning. To support health, therapeutic-grade essential oils can be applied topically, aromatically, or internally.

Essential oils are used in the perfume, flavoring, and aromatherapy industries. While essential oils used in the perfume industry (which may be diluted or adulterated with chemical ingredients) should never be used internally, therapeutic-grade essential oils represent the highest quality of essential oils on the market, and certain of these oils are safe to use internally. To ensure high standards, therapeutic-grade essential oils are tested throughout production. Before taking an oil internally, look up the oil in *Modern Essentials: A Contemporary Guide to the Therapeutic Use of Essential Oils* to learn more about the essential oil's uses. Also see the Essential Oils and Blends Quick Usage Chart in the appendix .

TOPICAL APPLICATION

Topical application is the process of placing an essential oil on the skin, hair, mouth, teeth, nails, or mucus membranes of the body. Since essential oils are so potent and because some essential oils may irritate the skin, the oils are often diluted with a pure vegetable oil, such as fractionated coconut oil, almond oil, olive oil, and jojoba oil. Topical application is most commonly used to benefit the immune system, cardiovascular system, muscles, bones, skin, and hair. Topical application can also be used to cleanse surfaces within the home.

AROMATIC APPLICATION

Aromatic application involves inhaling either a fine mist of the oil or a vapor of volatile aromatic components that have evaporated from the oil. Aromatic application is often used to support the nervous system, respiratory system, digestive system, and emotional balance. Aromatic application can also be used to eradicate unpleasant odors and help purify the air.

INTERNAL USE

Internal use of essential oils is the process of consuming or otherwise internalizing an essential oil into the body. Only pure, therapeutic-grade essential oils should be used for internal consumption, as other essential oils on the market may be diluted or processed using harmful chemicals. Internal application is often used to help benefit the digestive system, hormonal system, immune system, nervous system, and the body as a whole.

NOTES:

COOKING WITH ESSENTIAL OILS —FAQS AND TIPS

ONE GREAT WAY TO GIVE YOUR BODY THE BENEFITS OF ESSENTIAL OILS IS TO ADD THEM TO YOUR COOKING. ESSENTIAL OILS CAN PROVIDE AMAZING FLAVOR TO ANY DISH! THIS SECTION SHARES SOME HANDY ESSENTIAL OIL COOKING TIPS AND ANSWERS SOME COMMON QUESTIONS ABOUT USING ESSENTIAL OILS IN COOKING RECIPES.

IS IT SAFE TO INGEST ESSENTIAL OILS?

Not all essential oils are safe to ingest. There are a few things you want to know about your essential oils before using them in your cooking. First, you should only use high quality, pure, therapeutic-grade essential oils. Second, the label on your essential oil should state whether or not it is safe to use internally. A good indication is if the label lists supplement facts (which looks like the standard nutrition information label). If you are still unsure of whether your oil is safe to take internally, *Modern Essentials: A Contemporary Guide* lists this information under the Single Essential Oils or Essential Oil Blends sections.

Another thing to consider is who you are feeding. Children or pregnant or nursing women may be cautioned against ingesting certain oils. It is always wise to check label instructions for warnings and recommended use, or consult with a certified health care professional for further questions.

However, when using essential oils in cooking, the oils are generally diluted enough and used in small enough quantities that if using essential oils from spices, herbs, or citrus fruits that are commonly used in cooking, the food should be safe for all to eat.

WHAT ARE THE BENEFITS OF USING ESSENTIAL OILS IN COOKING?

Essential oils provide incredible flavor to food with just a drop of oil. Depending on the part of the plant the oil was extracted from and where the plant was grown, sometimes essential oils provide different flavors than when using fresh herbs. Also, some fresh herbs can be difficult to obtain, so you have access to a wider variety of flavors when incorporating essential oils in your spice rack.

Essential oils can be more cost effective than fresh or dried herbs in the long run because only a small amount is needed and oils stay good longer than fresh or dried herbs. Do your fresh herbs go bad because you can't use them fast enough?

Essential oils have a myriad of health benefits that your body can utilize when you use them in your food. To find out more about the benefits of essential oils, please refer to *Modern Essentials: A Contemporary Guide.*

WHAT OILS CAN BE USED IN COOKING?

Essential oils that come from spices, herbs, or citrus fruits commonly used in cooking are the best essential oils to incorporate in your food. These oils can include the following:

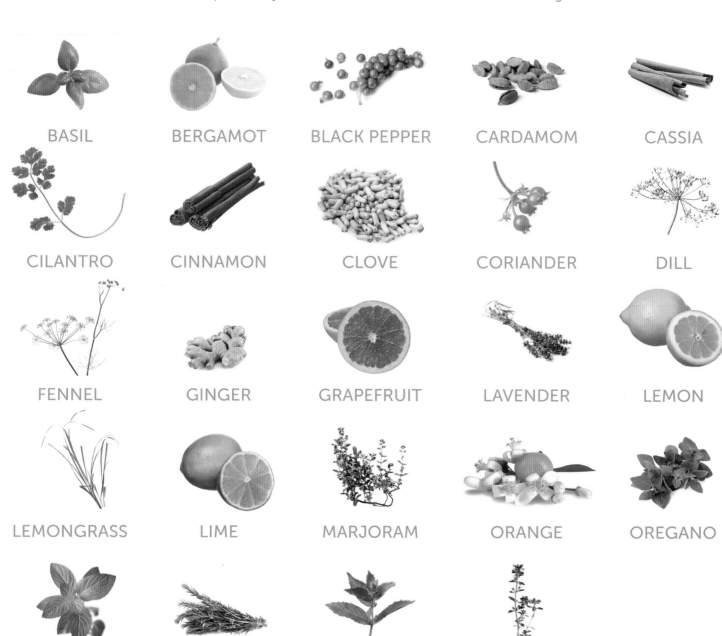

BASIL	BERGAMOT	BLACK PEPPER	CARDAMOM	CASSIA
CILANTRO	CINNAMON	CLOVE	CORIANDER	DILL
FENNEL	GINGER	GRAPEFRUIT	LAVENDER	LEMON
LEMONGRASS	LIME	MARJORAM	ORANGE	OREGANO
PEPPERMINT	ROSEMARY	SPEARMINT	THYME	

HOW MUCH OIL DO I SUBSTITUTE FOR HERBS?

How much oil to substitute for an herb varies quite a bit depending on the essential oil. Essential oils are very concentrated, so you only need a little bit—typically a drop or two. Some oils are really strong, and you may only need to dip a toothpick in the oil and then stir the toothpick into your mixture.

The number of drops needed in a recipe can also differ based on a number of factors, such as when the oils are added, the kind of food or beverage you are preparing, the strength of the oil, and your taste preferences.

If you are adding the oils at the end of cooking, smaller amounts are needed than if adding before baking, simmering, or steaming because oils tend to start to evaporate under heat. It is generally better to stir the essential oil in at the end of cooking or when the food has cooled; but some oils such as basil, marjoram, oregano, rosemary, and thyme are quite strong and may actually benefit from cooking a little to get a milder flavor.

One thing to keep in mind is that oil flavors tend to get stronger the longer the food or beverage has to "steep." If you are preparing something that will sit in the fridge for a day or two before you eat or drink it, you may want to add your oils an hour or two before serving instead of when you prepare the food or beverage.

OIL SUBSTITUTION GUIDELINES

 Typically, 1 drop of a citrus oil can substitute for 1 tsp. of citrus zest. If the recipe calls for the zest from 1 citrus fruit, you can use 3–10 drops of the citrus essential oil instead.

 For minty oils such as peppermint and spearmint, try substituting 1 drop of essential oil for 1 tsp. dried mint leaves or 1 Tbsp. fresh mint leaves.

 Cinnamon and cassia are pretty similar, and typically what we know as ground cinnamon is really ground cassia; however, the strength of their flavor is quite a bit different. You will want to start by substituting 1 drop of cinnamon for 1–2 Tbsp. ground cinnamon and 1 drop of cassia for 1 tsp. ground cinnamon or cassia.

 For herbaceous oils like basil, marjoram, oregano, rosemary, cilantro, dill, etc., start with a toothpick dipped in the oil and stirred into the mixture, and then add more to taste as needed.

 Floral herbs like lavender can be used in cooking; but because floral flavors are uncommon, you want just a hint of this flavor. Start with a toothpick, and add more if needed.

 For other flavors, a good rule of thumb is to substitute 1 drop of oil for 1–2 tsp. of dried spice or herb and 1 drop of oil for 1–2 Tbsp. of fresh spice. If you think the oil is strong or if the recipe calls for less than the above quantities, start with a toothpick dip instead. Taste, and add more if needed.

COOKING TIPS:

1. Know what part of the plant the oil came from. Citrus oils are pressed from the peel, so they can substitute for the zest but not the juice.
2. Getting the exact amount of oil drops can be tricky due to the different viscosity levels of the oils. If using the regular bottle with the orifice reducer, place your drops on a spoon; then stir into your mixture to ensure you have the right amount.
3. Putting your cooking oils in dropper bottles allows you to easily control the number of drops used and provides sufficient space to dip a toothpick into the oil when needed.
4. A little goes a long way. Start with only a drop of oil, taste, and repeat until you are satisfied with the flavor. Some oils are really strong, and a toothpick dipped in the oil, then stirred into your mixture, may be sufficient.

5. Use glass or stainless steel mixing bowls. Try to avoid plastic cookware, as the oils can damage certain types of plastic.
6. Always keep your oils away from heat, light, and humid conditions to maintain a long shelf life. Refrigerator storage is fine.
7. Make sure to recap your bottles so the oils don't evaporate out.
8. Because oils are altered by heat and may evaporate, it is always best to add the oils at the end of cooking if possible.
9. Give a subtle hint of herbs to your savory baked goods by creating a spray in a 4 oz. glass trigger spray bottle. Add a few drops of essential oil and 1/8 cup of olive oil to the spray bottle, and then fill the bottle the rest of the way with distilled water. Use this mixture to spray items like empanadas, tortilla chips, baked French fries, egg rolls, etc.
10. If you are baking with kids, make sure to keep the oils out of their reach.

NOTES:

○ COOKING:
APPETIZERS, SNACKS, MISC.

FLAVORED POPCORN

APPETIZERS, SNACKS, MISC.

YOUR CHOICE OF ESSENTIAL OIL

FLAVORED POPCORN

Servings: 4–5   Time: 5–10 minutes active   Difficulty: Easy

INGREDIENTS:

- 1/2 cup of unpopped popcorn (12–16 cups popped popcorn)
- 1/8–1/4 cup unrefined coconut oil
- 3–6 drops essential oil of your choice
- Sweetener such as honey or maple syrup to taste
- Salt to taste

INSTRUCTIONS:

1. Pop popcorn kernels, and then place popped popcorn in a large bowl or brown paper bag.
2. Heat coconut oil and sweetener over low heat until well combined and liquified. Remove from heat, and let cool for a couple minutes. Stir in essentials oils.
3. Pour coconut oil mixture over popcorn, and stir or shake to combine.
4. Add salt to taste.

FLAVOR IDEAS

COCONUT-LIME: 4–5 drops lime essential oil, 1–2 Tbsp. honey, and salt to taste.

SWEET SPICE: 3–4 drops Protective Blend (can replace with 2 drops clove and 2 drops orange essential oil) and 2 drops cinnamon essential oil with 2 Tbsp. maple syrup.

WHITE CHOCOLATE–PEPPERMINT: 4–6 drops peppermint essential oil and melted white chocolate.

LEMON & BROWNED BUTTER: Brown 6 Tbsp. butter (instead of coconut oil) in a saucepan; add 2–4 drops lemon essential oil.

PARMESAN–ROSEMARY: 1/2 cup grated Parmesan, 3 Tbsp. olive oil (instead of coconut oil), 2 tsp. salt, and 1 drop of rosemary essential oil. Mix olive oil and rosemary essential oil; add to popcorn, and then shake to coat. Slowly add the Parmesan and salt while shaking the popcorn.

GARLIC & HERBS: 4 Tbsp. melted butter (instead of coconut oil), 1–2 toothpicks each of rosemary and thyme essential oils, garlic powder (or finely chopped garlic lightly cooked in butter), and parsley flakes. Mix melted butter and essential oil; add to popcorn, and shake to coat. Slowly add garlic powder and parsley flakes while shaking the popcorn.

FROZEN YOGURT BITES

Servings: 2 cups   Time: 10 minutes active; 2 hours inactive   Difficulty: Easy

INGREDIENTS:

- 1/2 cup fruit of choice
- 1/2 cup plain Greek yogurt
- 1 drop citrus essential oil (lemon, orange, lime, etc.)
- 1/4 cup orange juice
- 1 envelope unflavored gelatin (about 1 Tbsp.)

INSTRUCTIONS:

1. Prepare a cookie sheet by placing parchment paper on the sheet (if the paper tends to roll, add small weights to the corners).
2. Place fruit in a food processor, and blend to desired consistency.
3. Mix fruit, yogurt, and essential oil together in a small bowl.
4. Place orange juice in a saucepan. Sprinkle gelatin over the liquid. Let sit for a minute. Place saucepan over low heat, stirring constantly for about 3 minutes or until the gelatin is completely dissolved. Immediately whisk the orange juice into the fruit and yogurt mix.
5. Pour the yogurt mix into a plastic bag. Cut a small piece off a corner of the bag, and pipe the yogurt onto the prepared cookie sheet in bite-sized increments.
6. Place the cookie sheet in the freezer for a couple hours. Once frozen, quickly peel the yogurt bites off the cookie sheet, and place them in a plastic freezer bag. Keep the yogurt bites frozen until you are ready to serve them, as they will start to melt after 10 minutes.

NOTE: The orange juice and gelatin mixture is optional, but adding the gelatin helps the yogurt bites keep their shape longer. If you are giving these to younger children, adding this small amount of gelatin is especially helpful because younger children take longer to eat the yogurt bites before they thaw.

FROZEN YOGURT BITES

APPETIZERS, SNACKS, MISC.
CITRUS ESSENTIAL OILS (LEMON, ORANGE, LIME, ETC.)

CREAMY FRUIT DIP

Time: **10 minutes active**   Difficulty: **Easy**

INGREDIENTS:

- 1 package (8 oz.) cream cheese, softened
- 1 cup (8 oz.) sour cream
- 1/3 cup white sugar
- 2 tsp. vanilla extract
- 3–4 drops lemon essential oil

INSTRUCTIONS:

Mix all ingredients together with an electric hand mixer until smooth. Serve with your choice of fresh fruits.

LEMON PINEAPPLE CHEESEBALL

Servings: 10   Time: 10 minutes active; 2 hours inactive   Difficulty: Easy

INGREDIENTS:

- 2 packages (8 oz.) cream cheese (room temperature)
- 1 1/2 cups grated cheddar cheese
- 1 package ranch dressing mix
- 2 drops lemon essential oil
- 1 cup pineapple, finely chopped
- 2 cups chopped pecans

INSTRUCTIONS:

1. Combine cream cheese, grated cheese, ranch dressing mix, and lemon essential oil in a large bowl. Stir until well incorporated.
2. Stir in chopped pineapple.
3. Form the mixture into a ball.
4. Roll the ball in chopped pecans.
5. Wrap the cheeseball in plastic wrap, and refrigerate for 2 hours or overnight.
6. Serve cheeseball with your choice of crackers.

HEARTY & WHOLESOME GRANOLA BARS

Servings: 12–14   Time: 10–15 minutes active; 1 hour inactive   Difficulty: Medium

INGREDIENTS:

- 1 1/2 cups mashed ripe banana (about 3 bananas)
- 1 tsp. pure vanilla extract
- 1/8–1/4 cup maple syrup (optional)
- 3–4 drops orange essential oil
- 2 cups rolled oats
- 1/2–3/4 cup dried cranberries
- 1/2 cup walnuts
- 1/2–3/4 cup almonds
- 1/2 cup sunflower seeds
- 1/2 cup pepita seeds (shelled pumpkin seeds)
- 1/4 cup hulled hemp seeds
- 1 tsp. cinnamon (or 1 toothpick cinnamon essential oil added to the wet ingredients)
- 1/4 tsp. sea salt, or to taste

INSTRUCTIONS:

1. Preheat the oven to 350 degrees Fahrenheit. Lightly grease a large rectangular baking dish (approx. 8.5" x 12.5"), and line it with a piece of parchment paper so the bars are easier to lift out.
2. In a large bowl, mash the bananas until smooth. Stir in the vanilla, maple syrup, and orange essential oil.
3. Place the rolled oats into a food processor (or blender on the lowest speed), and pulse until the oats are coarsely chopped (but still with lots of texture). Stir oats into the banana mixture.
4. Place the dried cranberries, walnuts, and almonds into the food processor or blender, and pulse until the nuts and fruit are coarsely chopped.
5. Combine the nuts, fruit, and the rest of the ingredients in a bowl, and stir together; then stir everything into the banana-oat mixture until thoroughly combined.
6. Spoon mixture into a prepared baking dish. Press down until compacted, and smooth out with hands until even. Use a pastry roller to smooth out if desired.
7. Bake for 25–30 minutes until firm and lightly golden along the edges. Place dish on cooling rack for 10 minutes; then lift the bars out by lifting the parchment paper. Place granola slab on a cooling rack, and allow to cool completely.
8. Slice into bars, and enjoy!

HEARTY & WHOLESOME GRANOLA BARS

APPETIZERS, SNACKS, MISC.

ORANGE & CINNAMON ESSENTIAL OILS

CILANTRO LIME DIPPING SAUCE

Servings: 9   Time: 10 minutes active   Difficulty: Easy

INGREDIENTS:

- 1/2 bunch of cilantro
- 1 half red onion
- 3 tomatillos, husks removed
- 1 avocado, peel and pit removed
- 1 tsp. garlic clove, minced
- 1 tsp. salt
- 1 tsp. lime juice
- 1 drop lime essential oil
- 1/2 cup sour cream or plain yogurt

INSTRUCTIONS:

1. Place all ingredients in a blender of food processor, and pulse until smooth.
2. Serve with Southwestern Egg Rolls (page 32).

CREAMY CUCUMBER DILL DRESSING

Servings: 1 cup   Time: 5 minutes active   Difficulty: Easy

INGREDIENTS:

- 1 seedless cucumber, chopped into chunks
- 4 Tbsp. sour cream or plain Greek yogurt
  (or a combination of the two) Note: Add
  more if you like a thicker dressing.
- 1 Tbsp. olive oil
- 1 Tbsp. distilled white vinegar
- 1 drop dill essential oil or 1 Tbsp. dried dill weed
- 1/4 tsp. garlic powder
- Black pepper to taste
- Salt to taste

INSTRUCTIONS:

1. Put everything in a blender, and blend until smooth. Add spices to taste, and blend for a few more seconds.
2. Chill in the refrigerator, or serve immediately.

COWBOY SALSA

APPETIZERS, SNACKS, MISC.

CILANTRO & LIME ESSENTIAL OILS

COWBOY SALSA

Servings: **8**   Time: **20 minutes active**   Difficulty: **Easy**

INGREDIENTS:

- 3 cups fresh tomatoes, diced
- 1/2 cup white or yellow onion, diced
- 1/2 cup red onion, diced
- 1/2 cup cilantro, chopped
- 1 can black beans (8 oz.), drained and rinsed
- 1 can corn (8 oz.), drained
- 2 tsp. lime juice
- 2 drops lime essential oil
- 1 toothpick cilantro essential oil (dip a toothpick into the oil, and then stir it into the salsa)
- Garlic salt

INSTRUCTIONS:

1. Mix together tomatoes, onions, cilantro, black beans, and corn.
2. Stir in lime juice and essential oils.
3. Add garlic salt to taste.
4. Serve with tortilla chips.

SOUTHWESTERN EGG ROLLS

Yield: 18 egg rolls   Time: 30 minutes active; 15 minutes inactive   Difficulty: Medium

INGREDIENTS:

- 1 pound ground beef, browned
- 1 cup cooked rice
- 1 cup cooked black beans, drained and rinsed
- 1 cup cooked corn
- 1 tsp. chili powder
- 1 tsp. ground cumin
- 1/4 tsp. salt
- 1 drop black pepper essential oil
- 18 egg roll wrappers

INSTRUCTIONS:

1. In a medium-sized mixing bowl, combine cooked ground beef with rice, beans, and corn. Stir in chili powder, cumin, salt, and black pepper essential oil.
2. Preheat oven to 425 degree Fahrenheit.
3. Place a small amount of the rice and bean mixture diagonally on the center of an egg roll wrapper. Dip your finger in water, and then run your finger over the bottom corner of the wrapper. Fold over the top corner of the wrapper to cover the mixture; then fold over the sides and roll tightly (the water on the bottom corner should help the wrapper to seal shut). Repeat until you have filled all of the egg rolls. Hint: Make sure to roll your egg rolls tightly and neatly so that the mixture doesn't fall out when you are cooking them or eating them.
4. Place the egg rolls on a greased baking sheet, and lightly brush them with olive oil.
5. Bake the egg rolls for 10–15 minutes (turning over once halfway through), or until lightly browned.
6. Serve egg rolls with Cilantro Lime Dipping Sauce (page 28).

SOUTHWESTERN EGG ROLLS

APPETIZERS, SNACKS, MISC.

BLACK PEPPER ESSENTIAL OIL

APPLE BUTTER

APPETIZERS, SNACKS, MISC.

CINNAMON & CLOVE ESSENTIAL OILS

APPLE BUTTER

Yield: Roughly 1 pint   Time: 15–60 minutes active; 12–14 hours inactive   Difficulty: Medium

INGREDIENTS:

- 3 lbs of apples, peeled, cored, and sliced (roughly 6 large apples or 10–12 small apples)
- 1 cup organic apple juice (no sugar added)
- 1/4 cup sugar (optional)
- 1/2 tsp. cinnamon powder
- 1/4 tsp. nutmeg
- 1/2 tsp. kosher salt
- 1 tsp. lemon juice
- 1/2 tsp. vanilla
- 1 toothpick cinnamon essential oil
- 1 toothpick clove essential oil

INSTRUCTIONS:

1. Put everything except the essential oils in a slow cooker, and cook for 10 hours on the low setting (cooking overnight works well).
2. After 10 hours of cooking, blend the apple mixture in a blender or with an immersion blender within the slow cooker. Cook for another 2 hours with the lid slightly ajar so steam can exit.
3. Check for doneness by putting a spoonful on a plate. Wait a minute or two. If a ring of liquid appears around your spoonful of apple butter, then it needs to continue cooking.
4. If your apple butter is not done yet, continue cooking it in the slow cooker, checking on it every 10 minutes and more frequently the thicker it gets.
5. If you want the apple butter to be done faster, you can transfer it to a saucepan and cook it over medium heat. Use a lid to contain the splatters, and lift the lid every couple minutes to let the steam escape, or prop the lid up with a chopstick. Remove from heat to stir every so often and check for doneness. When it stops splattering, it should be really close to being done.
6. Once the apple butter has thickened, remove from heat and allow to cool for 10 minutes. Dip the toothpicks in the essential oils, and stir into the apple butter.
7. Pour the apple butter into a pint-size jar, and refrigerate.

NOTES:

⬤ COOKING: BEVERAGES

FRUIT SMOOTHIES

BEVERAGES

LEMON, ORANGE, & GRAPEFRUIT ESSENTIAL OILS

PROTEIN FRUIT SMOOTHIE

Servings: 1   Time: 5 minutes active   Difficulty: Easy

INGREDIENTS:

- 1 whole banana, peeled
- 3 large strawberries
- 1 1/2 cups orange juice
- 2 drops orange, grapefruit, or lemon essential oil
- 2 Tbsp. peanut butter (for protein)
- 3 ice cubes

INSTRUCTIONS:

1. Put all ingredients in the blender, and blend until smooth.

LEMON BERRY GREEN SMOOTHIE

Servings: 3–4   Time: 5 minutes active   Difficulty: Easy

INGREDIENTS:

- 1 frozen banana
- 3 cups frozen mixed berries (strawberries, raspberries, blueberries)
- 1/2 cup frozen apple juice concentrate
- 2 handfuls fresh spinach
- 2 1/2 cups water
- 1 drop lemon essential oil

INSTRUCTIONS:

1. Place all ingredients in a blender, and blend until smooth. If you choose to use fresh fruit instead of frozen fruit, reduce the amount of water, and add some ice instead.
2. Serve immediately. Enjoy!

SPICED APPLE CIDER

Servings: **6; Makes 1/2 gallon**   Time: **15 minutes active; 3 hours inactive**   Difficulty: **Easy**

INGREDIENTS:

- 5 red apples
- 1/2 cup white sugar
- 1/2 Tbsp. ground allspice
- 2 drops cassia essential oil

INSTRUCTIONS:

1. Wash apples thoroughly, remove the cores, and cut them into quarters.
2. Place apples in a large stock pot, and add sugar and allspice.
3. Add enough water to the pot to cover the apples by 3–4 inches.
4. Boil the apples, uncovered, for one hour, stirring occasionally; then reduce heat, and simmer for two hours.
5. Strain out the cider by pouring the mixture through a fine mesh sieve.
6. Stir in cassia essential oil.
7. Serve cider warm, or refrigerate and serve chilled.

SPICED APPLE CIDER

BEVERAGES

CASSIA ESSENTIAL OIL

BASIC SPARKLING LIMEADE

BEVERAGES

LIME ESSENTIAL OIL

BASIC SPARKLING LIMEADE

Servings: 4–6   Time: 10 minutes active   Difficulty: Easy

INGREDIENTS:

- 1/2 cup lime juice (from about 3–4 limes; add water to reach 1/2 cup if needed)
- 1/2 cup sugar
- 1–2 drops lime essential oil
- Chilled sparkling water or club soda (Regular water works well if you don't like carbonation.)

INSTRUCTIONS:

1. Stir the lime juice in with the sugar in a small saucepan, and bring to a simmer over medium heat. Lower the heat, and cook (stirring frequently) until the sugar is completely dissolved. Remove from heat, and pour into a glass dish.
2. Add lime essential oil. Cover, and refrigerate until chilled.
3. Mix about 2 Tbsp. of limeade concentrate with 8 oz. of chilled sparkling water in a glass cup. Taste, and add more water if you want a lighter flavor.
4. Serve with ice.

FLAVOR VARIATIONS:

BASIL LIMEADE: Add 1 toothpick of basil essential oil with the lime essential oil, and use basil leaves for garnish.

ROSEMARY LIMEADE: Add 1 toothpick of rosemary essential oil with the lime essential oil, and use fresh sprigs of rosemary for garnish.

BASIC LEMONADE: Use 1/2 cup of lemon juice and 1–2 drops lemon essential oil instead of the lime juice and lime essential oil.

ROSEMARY CITRUS SPRITZER: Use 1/2 cup of lemon juice or 1/4 cup each of lemon and orange juice with 1–2 drops of lemon essential oil instead of the lime juice and lime essential oil. Add 1 toothpick of rosemary essential oil when adding the lemon essential oil. Garnish with fresh sprigs of rosemary.

STRAWBERRY BASIL SODA: Juice or blend 1/2 lb of strawberries. Strain out seeds and pulp. You should have 1/2 cup of strawberry juice. Add juice from half a lemon. Use the strawberry-lemon juice instead of the lime juice in the recipe, and use just 1 toothpick of basil essential oil instead of the lime essential oil.

STRAWBERRY LEMONADE

Servings: 8   Time: **10 minutes active**   Difficulty: **Easy**

INGREDIENTS:

- 4 cups of strawberries
- 4 cups of cold water
- Juice of one lemon
- 4–8 drops of lemon essential oil
- Agave or raw sugar, if desired

INSTRUCTIONS:

1. Puree the strawberries in a blender (you can add a tablespoon of water to help it puree more easily).
2. Pour the water into a quart-size pitcher.
3. Add the pureed strawberries, the juice of one lemon, and 4–8 drops of lemon essential oil (to taste).
4. Add agave or another sweetener as desired.
5. Mix well, and serve chilled.

STRAWBERRY LEMONADE

BEVERAGES

LEMON ESSENTIAL OIL

NOTES:

⬤ COOKING: SIDE DISHES

RAINBOW GARDEN SALAD

Yield: 4–6   Time: 30–40 minutes active   Difficulty: Easy

INGREDIENTS:

- Grape tomatoes, cut in half
- Carrots, peeled and sliced
- Sweet yellow peppers or yellow bell peppers, diced
- Cheddar cheese, shredded
- Lettuce of choice, shredded
- Cucumber, diced
- Broccoli, cut small
- Red cabbage leaves, cut in thin slices
- 1/2 cup quinoa, rinsed
- 1 cup water
- 1–2 drops lemon essential oil

INSTRUCTIONS:

1. Place water and quinoa in a small pot, and bring to a boil over medium heat. Boil for 5 minutes. Reduce heat to low, and simmer for 10 minutes. Add lemon essential oil, fluff with a fork, and continue cooking for 5 more minutes or until the quinoa has absorbed all the water.
2. Meanwhile, wash and cut the vegetables and other salad ingredients, and mix or stack the ingredients in a salad bowl or on a plate.

NOTE: It is best to prepare the dressing first so it has at least 30 minutes to sit in the refrigerator and allow the flavors to mix while you prepare the salad

CREAMY LEMON BASIL DRESSING

Servings: 8   Time: 10 minutes active; 30 minutes inactive   Difficulty: Easy

INGREDIENTS:

- 4 Tbsp. olive oil
- 3 Tbsp. lemon juice
- 1/2 cup sour cream or plain yogurt (or a combination of the two)
- 1/4 tsp. garlic powder
- 1/4 tsp. black pepper or 1 toothpick black pepper essential oil
- 1–2 drops basil essential oil

INSTRUCTIONS:

1. Whisk all ingredients together in a small bowl or blender bottle.
2. Allow to cool in the refrigerator for at least 30 minutes before serving.

RAINBOW GARDEN SALAD

SIDE DISHES

LEMON ESSENTIAL OIL

STUFFING

SIDE DISHES

ROSEMARY & THYME ESSENTIAL OILS

STUFFING

Servings: 4–6   Time: 25 minutes active; 2 hours inactive   Difficulty: Medium

INGREDIENTS:

- 8 slices bread
- 1/2 medium onion
- 1 stalk celery
- 6 Tbsp. butter
- 1 cup chicken broth
- 1/2 tsp. salt
- 1/8 tsp. pepper
- 1 tsp. dried sage
- 1 drop rosemary essential oil
- 1 drop thyme essential oil
- 2 eggs

INSTRUCTIONS:

1. Preheat oven to 350 degrees Fahrenheit. Using a serrated knife, cut bread into cubes.
2. Spread bread cubes out evenly on a baking sheet, and bake for 15–20 minutes, stirring once, until lightly golden.
3. Finely chop the onion and the celery. In a large saucepan, melt the butter, and then add the chopped onion and celery. Sauté the onion and celery over medium-high heat, stirring frequently, until barely tender.
4. Add the chicken broth, salt, pepper, and sage.
5. Remove saucepan from heat, and stir in essential oils.
6. Add the toasted bread chunks, and stir until evenly coated.
7. Stir in two eggs; and then spoon the stuffing into a greased casserole dish.
8. Bake stuffing at 350 degrees Fahrenheit for 25 minutes, or until the egg is cooked and the stuffing is a nice golden color.
9. Serve warm.

CILANTRO LIME RICE

Servings: **6**   Time: **10 minutes active; 20 minutes inactive**   Difficulty: **Easy**

INGREDIENTS:

- 2 cups rice
- 4 cups water
- 1 tsp. garlic, minced
- 1 tsp. olive oil
- 1 Tbsp. chicken bouillon
- 2 Tbsp. lime juice
- 2 drops lime essential oil
- 1 toothpick cilantro essential oil (dip the toothpick in the oil, and then swish the toothpick around in the mixture)
- 3/4 cup fresh cilantro, chopped

INSTRUCTIONS:

1. In a medium-sized pot, combine the rice, water, garlic, olive oil, and chicken bouillon.
2. Heat the rice over medium-high heat until it comes to a boil, stirring occasionally.
3. Put the lid on the pot, and reduce the heat to low.
4. Let the rice simmer for 20 minutes or until fully cooked (don't remove the lid while the rice is cooking).
5. Remove the rice from the heat, take off the lid, and let it cool slightly.
6. Meanwhile, combine the lime juice, lime essential oil, and cilantro oil in a separate bowl.
7. Stir the oil and lime juice mixture into the rice.
8. Add the fresh cilantro, and stir it into the rice.
9. Serve immediately!

NOTE: This tangy rice is the perfect side dish to eat with beans, enchiladas, or any other Mexican dish. It is also delicious inside a burrito.

CILANTRO LIME RICE
SIDE DISHES
CILANTRO & LIME ESSENTIAL OILS

GUACAMOLE

SIDE DISHES

CILANTRO ESSENTIAL OIL

GUACAMOLE

Servings: 4   Time: 15 minutes active   Difficulty: Easy

INGREDIENTS:

- 4 small diced tomatoes
- 2 chopped jalapeños, seeds removed
- 2 Tbsp. minced cilantro
- 1 drop cilantro essential oil
- 2 minced green onions
- 2 Tbsp. lime juice
- A pinch of kosher salt
- 2 avocados, pitted and smashed

INSTRUCTIONS:

1. Combine all ingredients in a medium-sized bowl.
2. Serve with tortilla chips or your favorite Mexican dish.

NOTES:

○ COOKING: ENTRÉES

HOMEMADE EMPANADAS

Yield: **9 empanadas**   Time: **1 hour active; 1 hour, 10 minutes inactive**   Difficulty: **Medium**

DOUGH INGREDIENTS:

- 2 1/4 cups flour
- 1 1/2 tsp. salt
- 1/2 cup butter (cold)
- 1 egg
- 1/3 cup ice water
- 1 Tbsp. white distilled vinegar

FILLING INGREDIENTS:

- 1 tsp. olive oil
- 1/4 cup yellow onion, diced
- 1 cup ground beef, cooked
- 1 tsp. beef bouillon
- 1/2 cup water
- 1 tsp. minced garlic
- 1 drop marjoram essential oil
- 1 toothpick black pepper essential oil (dip the toothpick in the oil, and then stir the toothpick around in the meat mixture)
- Salt to taste
- 9 black olives
- 3 hardboiled eggs, peeled and sliced into three pieces each

INSTRUCTIONS:

1. In a large bowl, stir together the flour and salt.
2. Cut the butter into small chunks, and then add it to the flour mixture. Using your fingers or a pastry cutter, incorporate the butter into the flour. The mixture should resemble coarse meal when you are finished with just small butter lumps.
3. In a separate bowl, whisk together the egg, ice water, and vinegar. Stir the wet ingredients into the flour mixture just enough to moisten it.
4. Place the dough on a lightly floured surface, and knead it with your hands a couple of times.
5. Form the dough into a flat circle, wrap it with plastic wrap, and put it in the refrigerator to chill for an hour.
6. Preheat your oven to 400 degrees Fahrenheit.
7. Pour the olive oil into a medium-size frying pan. Add the diced onion, and sauté over medium heat until just tender.
8. Add the ground beef, bouillon, water, and garlic to the frying pan. Bring to a boil, and then reduce the heat and let simmer for a couple minutes.
9. Remove the meat mixture from the heat, and add marjoram essential oil, black pepper essential oil, and salt.
10. Once the dough has chilled properly, remove it from the fridge, and divide it into 9 equal balls. Roll each piece of dough as thin as you can into a circle.
11. Place some of the meat mixture on one half of the dough circle, and place a slice of egg and an olive on top.
12. Dip your finger in water, and run it along one side of the dough circle to help the empanada seal shut.
13. Fold the dough over to make a half circle, and use your fingers to seal the edge. Repeat until all of the empanadas have been filled.
14. Place the prepared empanadas on a greased baking sheet, and bake them for 10 minutes, or until the bottoms are lightly browned and the tops are barely golden.
15. Let cool for a few minutes and then serve warm. You can serve the empanadas alone or with your choice of dipping sauce.
16. Enjoy!

MEDITERRANEAN HERBED SHISH KEBABS

ENTRÉES

MARJORAM, ROSEMARY, & THYME ESSENTIAL OILS

MEDITERRANEAN HERBED SHISH KEBABS

Servings: 6 shish kebabs   Time: 35 minutes active; 2 hours inactive   Difficulty: Easy

INGREDIENTS:

- 1/4 cup olive oil
- 1/4 cup lemon juice
- 1/4 cup white distilled vinegar
- 2 tsp. minced garlic clove
- 1 tsp. cumin powder
- 2 drops marjoram essential oil
- 2 drops thyme essential oil
- 3 drops rosemary essential oil
- 1/2 tsp. salt
- 1/4 tsp. black pepper
- 2 lbs boneless, skinless chicken breast
- 1 small zucchini
- 1 red onion
- 12 cherry tomatoes
- 12 mushrooms
- 6 wooden skewers

INSTRUCTIONS:

1. In a large zip-top bag, combine olive oil, lemon juice, vinegar, garlic, cumin, marjoram essential oil, thyme essential oil, rosemary essential oil, salt, and pepper.
2. Cut the chicken into 1-inch cubes, and place the cubes in the zip-top bag.
3. Seal the zip-top bag, and shake to evenly coat the chicken with the marinade. Refrigerate for at least 2 hours.
4. Slice the zucchini, and cut the onion into chunks.
5. Remove the chicken from the fridge. Using a slotted spoon, scoop the chicken out of the bag, and place it on a plate or in a bowl. Discard the marinade.
6. Thread the chicken and vegetables onto the wooden skewers. You can choose to put a combination of vegetables and chicken on each skewer, or you can cook the chicken and vegetables on separate skewers (this allows you to cook the chicken fully without overcooking the vegetables).
7. Sprinkle the vegetables lightly with salt, if desired.
8. Place skewers on a heated grill, and cook until the vegetables are tender and the chicken is cooked all the way through.
9. Remove from grill, and serve immediately!

CHICKEN COCONUT CURRY

Servings: 6–8   Time: 30 minutes active; 2–3 hours inactive   Difficulty: Medium

INGREDIENTS:

- 1 Tbsp. olive oil
- 1 medium sweet potato, peeled and diced
- 2 Tbsp. curry powder, divided
- 2 cans coconut milk (minus 1 cup for rice)
- 1 cup chicken broth
- 1 can tomato paste (6 oz.)
- 1 Tbsp Garam Masala
- Salt and pepper to taste
- 4–5 carrots, peeled and diced
- 1 medium onion, diced
- 3 cloves garlic, minced
- 1 large sweet pepper, diced or sliced into strips
- 2 chicken breasts, cut in small chunks
- 3 celery stalks, diced
- 2 small heads of broccoli, cut into florets
- 1 drop ginger essential oil
- 1 drop lemongrass essential oil

INSTRUCTIONS:

1. Heat olive oil in a saucepan over medium-high heat. Add sweet potato and 1 Tbsp. curry powder. Stir occasionally, and cook for 10 minutes or until the sweet potato is half cooked.
2. While the sweet potato is cooking, make the sauce. In a small bowl, mix together coconut milk, chicken broth, tomato paste, Garam Masala, 1 Tbsp. curry powder, salt, and pepper.
3. Add the carrots and onion, and continue to sauté until the onion is translucent.
4. Add garlic and sweet pepper, and continue to sauté for 1–2 minutes.
5. Transfer vegetable mixture to the slow cooker. Add chicken, celery, broccoli, and prepared sauce. Stir to combine.
6. Cook on low for 2–3 hours.
7. Once chicken is cooked through and vegetables are soft, stir in essential oils, and serve over rice.

NOTE: If sauce is too runny, mix together 6 Tbsp. water and 4 Tbsp. cornstarch or arrowroot powder in a small bowl, and then stir into curry.

CHICKEN COCONUT CURRY

ENTRÉES

GINGER & LEMONGRASS ESSENTIAL OILS

BASIL PESTO CHICKEN

ENTRÉES

BASIL & LEMON ESSENTIAL OILS

BASIL PESTO CHICKEN

Servings: 4–6   Time: 10 minutes active   Difficulty: Easy

INGREDIENTS:

- 8–12 oz. pasta of choice
- 1/4 cup olive oil, divided
- 2 garlic cloves, minced
- 2 cups spinach leaves, tough stems removed
- 1/4 cup pine nuts (almonds or walnuts can be used instead if needed)
- 2 Tbsp. lemon juice
- 2 drops lemon essential oil
- 1 drop basil essential oil
- 1/3 cup Parmesan cheese
- Salt and pepper to taste
- 2–3 chicken breasts, cooked and sliced or cubed

INSTRUCTIONS:

1. Boil water in a pot, and cook pasta according to the directions on the package.
2. Heat a little bit of olive oil in a saucepan over medium heat. Add the minced garlic, and sauté for 2 minutes.
3. Pack the spinach in the bottom of your blender. Press the spinach down as much as possible. Add pine nuts, sautéed garlic, olive oil, lemon juice, and essential oils on top of the spinach in the blender.
4. Blend the ingredients together by using the pulse setting on the blender and pausing to scrape the sides as needed.
5. Add Parmesan cheese, salt, and pepper, and blend in. Note: If you wish to freeze any of this pesto, you will want to freeze it before adding the Parmesan cheese.
6. Combine or layer pasta, chicken, and spinach-basil pesto, and enjoy!

EXTRA IDEA:
For additional flavor, marinate the chicken for 30–60 minutes before cooking in 1/4 cup olive oil, 2 Tbsp. lemon juice, 2 drops basil essential oil, 3 drops lemon essential oil, and a small handful of fresh basil leaves cut up.

MEDITERRANEAN CHICKEN LETTUCE WRAPS

Servings: 4–6   Time: 20–30 minutes active   Difficulty: Easy

INGREDIENTS:

- 1 Tbsp. olive oil
- 2 chicken breasts, sliced into strips
- 1/4 cup balsamic vinegar (A combination of red-wine vinegar and lemon juice tastes great too!)
- 1–2 drops basil essential oil
- 1–2 drops oregano essential oil
- 1–2 drops rosemary essential oil
- 1 drop black pepper essential oil
- Salt to taste
- Butter lettuce or iceberg lettuce leaves
- Grape tomatoes, halved
- Feta cheese, crumbled
- Tzatziki (see recipe on following page)
- Red onion, sliced thin
- Kalamata olives, pitted and chopped

INSTRUCTIONS:

1. If making the tzatziki, mix it now so that it can chill while you make the chicken and prepare the wraps.
2. Heat olive oil in a saucepan over medium heat. Add chicken breast strips, and allow to cook.
3. In a glass dish, combine the balsamic vinegar, essential oils, and salt. Mix until well incorporated.
4. Flip the chicken, and begin to cook on the other side. Pour balsamic vinegar mixture over the chicken, and continue to sauté until the chicken is fully cooked.
5. Prepare the lettuce and other toppings.
6. Assemble the lettuce wraps by placing the chicken and other toppings inside the lettuce leaf like you would assemble a taco.
7. Serve immediately.

Check out this healthy version of a Greek pita! However, if you like the bread, just assemble the ingredients into a pita, including the lettuce. The leftover tzatziki also makes a fantastic vegetable dip!

MEDITERRANEAN CHICKEN LETTUCE WRAPS

ENTRÉES

BASIL, OREGANO, ROSEMARY, BLACK PEPPER, & DILL ESSENTIAL OILS

TZATZIKI

Servings: **2 cups**   Time: **10 minutes active**   Difficulty: **Easy**

INGREDIENTS:

- 1 1/2 Tbsp. olive oil
- 1 Tbsp. white vinegar
- 1/4 tsp. garlic powder
- 1/4 tsp. salt
- 1/4 tsp. white pepper
- 1/2 cup plain Greek yogurt, strained
- 1/2 cup sour cream
- 1 cucumber, peeled, seeded, and diced small
- 1–2 drops dill essential oil

INSTRUCTIONS:

1. Mix olive oil, vinegar, garlic powder, salt, pepper, and 1 drop dill essential oil together.
2. Add Greek yogurt and sour cream. Mix until well incorporated.
3. Mix in cucumber, and add more dill essential oil to taste.
4. Refrigerate for an hour, ideally, before serving to allow flavors to mix.

BLACK BEAN QUINOA ENCHILADA CASSEROL

ENTRÉES

CUMIN, CILANTRO, & LIME ESSENTIAL OILS

BLACK BEAN QUINOA ENCHILADA CASSEROLE

Servings: 8–10   Time: 30 minutes active; 30 minutes inactive   Difficulty: Easy

INGREDIENTS:

- 2 cups water
- 1 cup uncooked quinoa, rinsed
- 1 Tbsp. olive oil
- 1 medium onion, diced
- 3–4 cloves garlic, minced
- 1–2 sweet peppers (red, orange, yellow, or green), seeds removed and diced
- 1 can sweet corn (15 oz. size) or 1 1/4 cup frozen corn kernels
- Juice of 1 lime
- 1 Tbsp. chili powder
- 1 drop cumin essential oil
- 1 drop cilantro essential oil
- 1 drop lime essential oil
- 1/4 cup chopped cilantro, optional
- Salt and pepper, to taste
- 2 cans black beans, drained and rinsed (15 oz. size)
- 1 can red enchilada sauce (20 oz. size; approximately 2 cups)
- 1 cup cheddar cheese and 1 cup mozzarella cheese, mixed and shredded (or 2 cups Mexican cheese)
- Additional toppings: sour cream, sliced avocado, green onions, or cilantro (optional)

NOTE: Another great way to cook the quinoa is to place 1 cup of quinoa and 1 3/4 cups water in a pressure cooker and cook on high for 7 minutes. Once done, release pressure and set aside (do not remove lid) until the rest of the enchilada mixture is done.

INSTRUCTIONS:

1. Place water and quinoa in a small pot, and bring to a boil over medium heat. Boil for 5 minutes. Reduce heat to low, and simmer for 10 minutes. Fluff with a fork, and continue cooking for 5 more minutes or until the quinoa has absorbed all the water.
2. Meanwhile, heat olive oil in a large saucepan over medium-high heat. Add diced onion, and sauté until softened. Add garlic and peppers. Cook for 3–4 more minutes.
3. Add corn, lime juice, chili powder, essential oils, and cilantro. Stir to combine, and season with salt and pepper to taste.
4. Mix in quinoa, black beans, enchilada sauce, and 1/2 cup shredded cheese mixture until well combined.
5. Preheat the oven to 350 degrees Fahrenheit.
6. Place the mixture into a greased 9×13 casserole dish. Top with remaining shredded cheese.
7. Cover the pan with foil. Bake for 20 minutes, and then remove foil and continue baking until cheese is melted and edges are bubbling.
8. Remove from the oven, and let cool for 10 minutes before serving. Garnish with additional toppings, if desired.

ASIAN BROCCOLI BEEF

ENTRÉES

GINGER ESSENTIAL OIL

ASIAN BROCCOLI BEEF

Servings 4   Time: 30 minutes active   Difficulty: Medium

INGREDIENTS:

- 1/2 cup soy sauce
- 3 Tbsp. water
- 2 Tbsp. brown sugar
- 2 Tbsp. cornstarch
- 1–2 drops ginger essential oil
- 1 1/2 lbs thin sliced steak
- 2 cups small broccoli florets

INSTRUCTIONS:

1. Combine the soy sauce, water, brown sugar, cornstarch, and ginger essential oil in a small bowl.
2. Pour the mixture over the sliced steak. Let marinate on the counter for at least 10 minutes.
3. Heat your pan, and stir fry the broccoli (about 5 minutes).
4. Remove broccoli from pan, and set aside.
5. Allow pan to get hot again, and add the meat in batches. Cook each batch for about five minutes, stirring occasionally, to brown both sides.
6. Once all the meat is cooked, add the remaining marinade and broccoli to the pan, and stir it in with your meat.
7. Cook until the mixture thickens.
8. Serve over your choice of white or brown rice.

HOMEMADE LASAGNA

Servings: 8–10   Time: 35 minutes active; 45 minutes inactive   Difficulty: Easy

INGREDIENTS:

- 1 lb ground beef
- 12 lasagna noodles
- 1 Tbsp. olive oil
- 1/2 white onion, finely chopped
- 1 tsp. garlic clove, minced
- 1 1/2 tsp. salt
- 2 cans crushed tomatoes (28 oz. size)
- 1 drop oregano essential oil
- 1 drop rosemary essential oil
- 1 drop thyme essential oil
- 1 container cottage cheese (24 oz. size)
- 16 oz. shredded mozzarella cheese

INSTRUCTIONS:

1. In a large saucepan, brown the ground beef. Once cooked, drain the ground beef, and set aside in another dish.
2. Bring a large pot of water to a boil, and then add the lasagna noodles. Cook until noodles are tender. Then remove from heat, drain, and set aside.
3. While the noodles are cooking, prepare the sauce. Place the olive oil and chopped onion in the saucepan, and sauté over medium heat until the onions are tender.
4. Add the garlic in with the onions, and continue cooking for an additional minute, stirring frequently.
5. Add the salt, crushed tomatoes, and cooked ground beef to the saucepan, stir everything in the saucepan together, and continue cooking until warmed through.
6. Turn off the heat, and stir in the oregano, rosemary, and thyme essential oils.
7. Preheat your oven to 375 degrees Fahrenheit.
8. Spray the bottom of a 9 x 13 casserole dish with cooking spray.
9. Assemble the lasagna in the casserole dish by layering noodles, sauce, cottage cheese, and grated mozzarella cheese. Continue layering until you have used all of the noodles and the casserole dish is full.
10. Cover the lasagna with aluminum foil, and bake for 45 minutes, or until hot and bubbly. Remove the foil for the last 15 minutes of baking.
11. Let the lasagna sit for about 15 minutes so that it cools slightly, and then serve!

HOMEMADE LASAGNA
ENTRÉES

OREGANO, ROSEMARY, & THYME ESSENTIAL OILS

SAVORY DINNER CREPES

ENTRÉES

ROSEMARY, THYME, & SAGE ESSENTIAL OILS

SAVORY DINNER CREPES

Servings: 15   Time: 60 minutes active; 2 hours inactive   Difficulty: Medium

CREPES INGREDIENTS:

- 1 cup cold milk
- 1 cup cold water
- 4 eggs
- 1/2 tsp. salt
- 1/2 cup flour
- Butter

INSTRUCTIONS:

1. Place all ingredients in a blender. Blend on high for about a minute or until the ingredients are completely combined.
2. Place batter in the fridge to chill for 1–2 hours.
3. Once chilled, remove the batter from the fridge, and use a crepe pan or a small frying pan to cook your crepes.
4. Lightly coat the pan with butter, and heat to medium-high. Pour a thin layer of batter into the pan. Cook until the crepe is golden on the bottom; then flip the crepe and cook the other side. Repeat until all the crepes are cooked.

FILLING INGREDIENTS:

- 2 cups of chicken, diced
- 1 tsp. olive oil
- 4 Tbsp. butter
- 2 Tbsp. flour
- 1 cup milk, warmed
- 2 tsp. garlic powder
- Salt and pepper
- 1 drop rosemary essential oil
- 1 drop thyme essential oil
- 1 drop sage essential oil
- Grated cheese

INSTRUCTIONS:

1. Sauté chicken in olive oil until cooked completely. Remove from pan, and set aside.
2. Using the same pan you cooked the chicken in, melt the butter, and then whisk in 2 Tbsp. of flour.
3. Gradually add the warm milk to create a creamy sauce. Add the garlic, salt, pepper, and essential oils. Taste, and add more salt and pepper if needed.
4. Return the chicken to the pan, and stir it in with the sauce.
5. Sprinkle cheese on the bottom of a crepe, layer chicken and sauce over it, and roll it up. Repeat until all of your crepes have been filled.
6. Serve immediately.

CREAMY BUTTERNUT SQUASH SOUP

Servings: 6   Time: 35 minutes active; 25 minutes inactive   Difficulty: Easy

INGREDIENTS:

- 1 Tbsp. butter
- 1 medium onion (diced)
- 4 fresh sage leaves (chopped)
- 1 large butternut squash (peeled, seeded, and cut into chunks)
- 6 cups vegetable or chicken broth
- 1/2 cup coconut milk
- 1–2 drops sage essential oil
- Kosher salt and garlic pepper

INSTRUCTIONS:

1. Heat the butter in a large pot over medium-high heat. After a minute, add the onion, and sauté until translucent.
2. Add fresh sage and squash, and cook until the squash begins to soften slightly.
3. Pour in the broth.
4. Bring the soup to a boil; then reduce the heat, and simmer about 20 minutes until the squash is tender.
5. Using a blender, blend small batches of the soup until smooth. Once all the soup is blended, return it to the pot, and warm the soup over low heat.
6. Stir in the coconut milk and sage essential oil. Add salt and garlic pepper to taste.
7. Enjoy!

CREAMY BUTTERNUT SQUASH SOUP

ENTRÉES

SAGE ESSENTIAL OIL

HONEY LIME CHICKEN MARINADE

ENTRÉES

LIME ESSENTIAL OIL

HONEY LIME CHICKEN MARINADE

Yield: 3/4 cup of marinade; enough for 1–2 lbs chicken   Time: 5 minutes active   Difficulty: Easy

MARINADE INGREDIENTS:

- 1/4 cup olive oil
- 1/4 cup lime juice
- 2 Tbsp. honey
- 1 tsp. kosher salt
- 1 tsp. black pepper
- 1/2 tsp. cayenne pepper
- 4–6 drops lime essential oil

GLAZE INGREDIENTS (OPTIONAL):

- 2–3 Tbsp. honey
- 1 Tbsp. lime juice
- 1 drop lime essential oil

INSTRUCTIONS:

1. Whisk all marinade ingredients together.
2. Place chicken in a baking dish, and pour marinade over; or place chicken and marinade in a sturdy zip-top bag, and shake to coat. Allow chicken to marinate for an hour before grilling.
3. If you like a stickier glaze, mix an additional 2–3 Tbsp. honey with 1 Tbsp. lime juice and 1 drop of lime essential oil, and brush onto chicken during the last 5 minutes of cooking.

HONEY ESSENTIAL OIL HAM GLAZE

Servings: 1 cup   Time: 5 minutes active; 20 minutes inactive   Difficulty: Easy

INGREDIENTS:

- 1 cup honey
- 1 tsp. dry mustard
- 1 drop clove essential oil
- 1 drop orange essential oil
- 1 toothpick cassia essential oil

INSTRUCTIONS:

1. Combine all ingredients in a glass bowl, and stir until well incorporated.
2. Drizzle the glaze over your ham 20 minutes before it is done cooking. Return your ham to the oven, and cook uncovered for the remaining 20 minutes.
3. If you desire, you can reserve some of the glaze to drizzle over your ham when serving.

HONEY ESSENTIAL OIL HAM GLAZE

ENTRÉES

CLOVE, ORANGE, & CASSIA ESSENTIAL OILS

NOTES:

○ COOKING: DESSERTS

INSIDE OUT PEPPERMINT PATTIES

Yield: 4 dozen   Time: 20 minutes active; 3 hours inactive   Difficulty: Easy

INGREDIENTS:

- 1 lb powdered sugar
  (about 4 1/4–4 3/4 cups)
- 4 oz. cream cheese, softened
- 7–14 drops peppermint essential oil
- 6 oz. semi-sweet chocolate chips

INSTRUCTIONS:

1. Using a mixer, gradually add the powdered sugar to the cream cheese.
2. Add peppermint essential oil.
3. Roll dough into small balls, and place on baking sheet(s) lined with wax paper or parchment. Create a small indention in each ball. Cover with plastic wrap, and refrigerate for 3 hours.
4. Melt chocolate in a double boiler. Fill a piping bag or freezer bag with the corner snipped with the melted chocolate. Fill each mini peppermint indention with chocolate, and let cool.
5. Keep refrigerated until ready to serve.

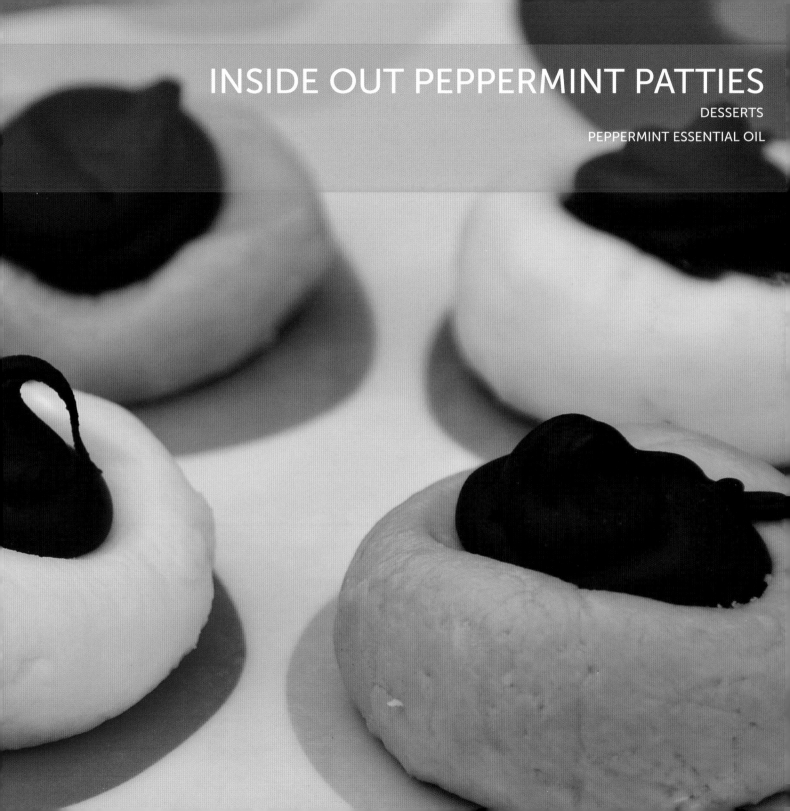

INSIDE OUT PEPPERMINT PATTIES

DESSERTS

PEPPERMINT ESSENTIAL OIL

GRASSHOPPER PIE

DESSERTS
PEPPERMINT ESSENTIAL OIL

GRASSHOPPER PIE

Servings: **8**   Time: **25 minutes active; 2 hours inactive**   Difficulty: **Easy**

INGREDIENTS:

- 24 chocolate sandwich cookies, crushed
- 1/4 cup butter, melted
- 2 packages cream cheese, softened
- 1 can sweetened condensed milk
- 2 cups whipped topping
- 4 drops peppermint essential oil

INSTRUCTIONS:

1. Combine crushed chocolate sandwich cookies (you can crush the cookies in a food processor or by hand in a zip-top bag) and melted butter in a medium-sized bowl. Stir until well incorporated.
2. Press cookie mixture into the bottom and sides of a pie pan to form a crust. Chill crust in the refrigerator for one hour.
3. In a large mixing bowl, combine cream cheese and sweetened condensed milk. Beat with an electric mixer for 5 minutes, ensuring that the mixture is light and fluffy.
4. Stir in whipped topping and peppermint essential oil.
5. Let pie chill for 1 hour before serving.
6. Enjoy!

ESSENTIAL OIL–INFUSED TRUFFLES

Yield: 36 truffles   Time: 30 minutes active; 10 minutes inactive   Difficulty: Easy

INGREDIENTS:

- 1 package chocolate sandwich cookies
- 1 package cream cheese (8 oz.), softened
- 5–8 drops peppermint essential oil
- 1 package semi-sweet chocolate chips (16 oz.)

INSTRUCTIONS:

1. Place all but 3 chocolate sandwich cookies in a food processor, and pulse until finely crushed.
2. Pour crushed cookies into a mixing bowl along with cream cheese and peppermint essential oil. Stir until combined and evenly moistened. Scoop the mixture out, and mold it into 1 inch balls.
3. Place truffle balls on a cookie sheet lined with wax paper. Place truffles in freezer for 10 minutes.
4. Melt chocolate chips in microwave. Remove the truffles from the freezer, and dip them in the melted chocolate. Evenly coat the truffles, and allow the excess chocolate to run off.
5. Return truffles to the baking sheet, and immediately sprinkle the tops with the 3 remaining cookies, crushed. Allow chocolate to set. Store covered in the refrigerator.

ESSENTIAL OIL–INFUSED TRUFFLES

DESSERTS

PEPPERMINT ESSENTIAL OIL

LEMON YOGURT FRUIT PARFAIT

Servings: **1**   Time: **5 minutes**   Difficulty: **Easy**

INGREDIENTS:

- 1/2 cup fresh or frozen berries
- 1 cup vanilla Greek yogurt
- 1 toothpick lemon essential oil
- 1 handful granola

INSTRUCTIONS:

1. Place berries in the bottom of a glass cup.
2. Measure out the Greek yogurt, and stir in 1 toothpick of lemon essential oil (dip a toothpick in the oil, and then stir the toothpick around in the yogurt).
3. Spoon the yogurt into the glass over the berries.
4. Sprinkle granola over top of the yogurt.
5. Enjoy!

STRAWBERRY ORANGE SORBET

Servings: 3–4   Time: 30 minutes active; 3–4 hours inactive

INGREDIENTS:

- 1 cup water
- 1/2 cup organic blue agave syrup
- 2 3/4 cups sliced strawberries
  (about 1 1/2 one-pint baskets)
- 1/2 cup fresh orange juice
- 2 drops orange essential oil

INSTRUCTIONS:

1. Stir together water and agave syrup in a small saucepan over medium heat, and bring to a boil.
2. Chill syrup mixture until cold (about 1 hour).
3. Combine sliced strawberries, fresh orange juice, and orange essential oil in a food processor or blender. Puree until smooth.
4. With the food processor running, gradually add the chilled syrup. Process until well blended.
5. Transfer sorbet to an ice cream maker, and freeze according to the manufacturer's directions.
6. If you don't have an ice cream maker, then transfer the mixture to a glass dish, and freeze just until the sorbet is firm, stirring every 30 minutes—about 3 hours total. Transfer the frozen sorbet from the glass dish into the processor, and puree until smooth.
7. Spoon the sorbet into dessert glasses, and serve immediately. Freeze leftovers in a covered container for up to 3 days.

CARROT CAKE

DESSERTS

CASSIA ESSENTIAL OIL

CARROT CAKE

Servings: 8–10   Time: 40 minutes active; 60 minutes inactive   Difficulty: Medium

CAKE INGREDIENTS:

- 2 cups sugar
- 1 1/4 cup canola oil
- 6 drops cassia essential oil
- 3 cups flour
- 2 tsp. baking soda
- 1/2 tsp. salt
- 2 cups grated carrot
- 1 small can crushed pineapple
  (Note: You can omit the pineapple and increase the grated carrot to 3 cups, if you prefer.)
- 2 tsp. vanilla
- 1/2 cup chopped walnuts
- 4 eggs

CREAM CHEESE FROSTING INGREDIENTS:

- 1 package cream cheese (8 oz.)
- 1/2 cup butter
- 1–3 drops lemon essential oil
- 1 package powdered sugar (16 oz.)
- 1 tsp. vanilla
- 1 cup chopped nuts
- 2 Tbsp. whipping cream

FUN FACT: Did you know that the ground cinnamon carried in most American grocery stores is actually ground cassia?

FROSTING INSTRUCTIONS:

1. Blend together cream cheese, butter, and lemon essential oil.
2. Then add powdered sugar, vanilla, and nuts.
3. Gradually add the whipping cream until the frosting reaches desired consistency.

CAKE INSTRUCTIONS:

1. Mix the sugar, canola oil, and cassia oil together in a bowl.
2. In a separate bowl, sift the flour, baking soda, and salt together.
3. Combine the sugar mixture and half of the flour mixture.
4. Beat in the carrots, pineapple, vanilla, and walnuts.
5. Add the rest of the flour mixture.
6. Add eggs, one at a time, beating well after each addition.
7. Pour into a greased and floured 9" x 13" cake pan.
8. Bake at 350 degrees Fahrenheit for 30–40 minutes or until a toothpick inserted in the center comes out clean.

FRUITY POPSICLES

DESSERTS

LEMON ESSENTIAL OIL

LEMON-BLUEBERRY POPS

Time: **5–10 minutes active; 3 hours inactive**   Difficulty: **Easy**

INGREDIENTS:

- 1 cup frozen blueberries
- 1/2 cup spinach
- 1 banana, peeled
- 1 apple, peeled, cored, and sliced
- 1/4 cup orange juice
- 3/4 cup coconut milk
- 1/4 cup plain Greek yogurt
- 1 drop lemon essential oil

INSTRUCTIONS:

1. Blend all ingredients together like a smoothie.
2. Pour into popsicle molds, and freeze for at least 3 hours or until solid.

FRESH & CHUNKY PEACH POPS

Time: **10 minutes active; 3 hours inactive**   Difficulty: **Easy**

INGREDIENTS:

- 3–4 medium ripe peaches, halved and pitted
- 1/4 cup orange juice
- Juice of 1 lemon
- 1/8 cup maple syrup or sugar, or to taste
- 1/4 tsp. vanilla extract
- 1 drop lemon or orange essential oil

INSTRUCTIONS:

1. Coarsely chop peaches in a food processor or blender, and set aside 1 cup.
2. Add the rest of the ingredients to the blender, and blend until smooth.
3. Mix in the coarsely chopped peaches, and pour into popsicle molds.
4. Freeze for at least 3 hours or until solid.

LUSCIOUS LEMON BARS

DESSERTS

LEMON ESSENTIAL OIL

LUSCIOUS LEMON BARS

Servings: 8   Time: 25 minutes active; 1 hour inactive   Difficulty: Easy

CRUST INGREDIENTS:

- 2 cups flour
- ½ cup sugar
- Dash of salt
- 1 cup butter

FILLING INGREDIENTS:

- 4 eggs
- 6 Tbsp. flour
- 1½ cup sugar
- 1 tsp. baking powder
- ¼ tsp. salt
- ½ cup lemon juice
- ½ cup water
- 3 drops lemon essential oil
- 1 Tbsp. powdered sugar
- Lemon zest (optional)

INSTRUCTIONS:

1. Preheat oven to 350 degrees Fahrenheit.
2. Mix together flour, sugar, and salt.
3. Cut in the butter until the dough reaches a fine crumb consistency.
4. Press the dough into the bottom of a 9 x 13 pan. Bake for 20 minutes or until golden.
5. While crust is baking, beat eggs in a large mixing bowl. In a separate dish, stir together flour, sugar, baking powder, and salt.
6. Add flour mixture to eggs, and stir till smooth.
7. Gradually stir in lemon juice, water, and lemon essential oil. Pour mixture over baked crust, and return to the oven.
8. Bake 30 minutes or until set.
9. Allow to cool completely, and sift powdered sugar over the top.
10. Garnish with zest if desired.

NOTE: Substitute orange oil and orange juice to make orange bars.

CINNAMON MUFFINS

Yield: 18 muffins   Time: 20 minutes active; 20 minutes inactive   Difficulty: Easy

MUFFIN BATTER INGREDIENTS:

- 1/2 cup vegetable oil
- 1 cup milk
- 1 1/2 cups sugar
- 1 tsp. salt
- 2 eggs, beaten
- 3 cups flour
- 1 Tbsp. baking powder
- 2 drops cassia essential oil

TOPPING INGREDIENTS:

- 1/2 cup brown sugar
- 2 tsp. cinnamon
- 2 Tbsp. flour
- 2 Tbsp. butter, softened

INSTRUCTIONS:

1. Preheat oven to 375 degrees Fahrenheit.
2. Combine all batter ingredients in a medium-size bowl, and stir until well combined.
3. Pour batter into greased muffin tins, filling each tin about 3/4 full.
4. In a small bowl, combine all topping ingredients. Spoon topping evenly over muffins.
5. Bake muffins for 12–16 minutes or until a toothpick inserted in the middle comes out clean.
6. Serve muffins warm.

CINNAMON MUFFINS

DESSERTS

CASSIA ESSENTIAL OIL

NOTES:

 CRAFTS

ESSENTIAL OIL GEL AIR FRESHENER
ESSENTIAL OIL SOLID PERFUME LOCKET
WOOL DRYER BALLS
CITRUS-SCENTED WAX MELTS
CLOTHESPIN CAR DIFFUSER
PINE CONE OWL DIFFUSER

ESSENTIAL OIL GEL AIR FRESHENERS

Yield: **2 air fresheners**   Time: **20 minutes active; 2 hours inactive**   Difficulty: **Easy**

INGREDIENTS AND MATERIALS NEEDED:

- 1 cup water
- 2 tsp. salt
- 1 pkg. unflavored gelatin (1/4 oz.)
- 2 glass salve jars (4 oz. size)
- 2 drops food coloring (if desired)
- 20 drops essential oil

INSTRUCTIONS:

1. In a small pot, combine water and salt. Bring to a boil.
2. Remove pot from heat, and add the gelatin pack. Stir with a fork or a whisk until the gelatin is completely dissolved.
3. Pour mixture into glass jars.
4. Add 1 drop of food coloring to each jar, and stir in with a toothpick.
5. Allow mixture to cool slightly, and then stir 10 drops of essential oil into each jar (we used lime essential oil and love how it turned out!).
6. Twist the lid on, and allow to set completely before using.
7. When you wish to use the air freshener, remove the lid, and set the jar in your desired location. This gel freshener works great for smaller room like bathrooms or offices.

ESSENTIAL OIL GEL AIR FRESHENERS

CRAFTS

YOUR CHOICE OF ESSENTIAL OIL

ESSENTIAL OIL SOLID PERFUME LOCKET

CRAFTS

YOUR CHOICE OF ESSENTIAL OIL

ESSENTIAL OIL SOLID PERFUME LOCKET

Yield: **3–4 lockets**   Time: **25 minutes active**   Difficulty: **Easy**

INGREDIENTS AND MATERIALS NEEDED:

- 1 Tbsp. beeswax
- 3 Tbsp. jojoba oil
- 3–4 drops vitamin E (optional)
- 90–120 drops essential oils

INSTRUCTIONS:

1. Pack grated beeswax or beeswax pellets into a Tablespoon-size measuring spoon until it is packed level with the top; then dump the beeswax into a heat-proof glass measuring cup.
2. Add 3 Tbsp. of jojoba oil to the beeswax.
3. Place the measuring cup in a large sauce pan that is filled with 1" of hot water.
4. Place the sauce pan and measuring cup on the stove, and turn the burner on low.
5. Stir the mixture in the measuring cup with a bamboo skewer every couple of minutes until the beeswax is completely melted (about 15–20 minutes).
6. Turn off the stove, and carefully remove the measuring cup from the pan. Place the measuring cup on a towel on a countertop or table.
7. Stir in the contents of 1 capsule of vitamin E (or 3–4 drops liquid vitamin E).
8. Allow the mixture to cool slightly, and then stir in 90–120 drops of your desired essential oil or blend. Note: You may find it easier to pre-measure the essential oil in another container and add it all at once.
9. Quickly pour the mixture into the lockets. This recipe will fill three or four lockets, depending on size.
10. Allow mixture to cool for several hours before wearing the locket. To use, take a small amount of the solid perfume from the locket with your finger, and place it on the wrists, the neck, or any other location on the skin that is desired.

WOOL DRYER BALLS

CRAFTS

YOUR CHOICE OF ESSENTIAL OIL

WOOL DRYER BALLS

Yield: 2 dryer balls   Time: 40 minutes active; 3–4 hours inactive   Difficulty: Medium

---

MATERIALS NEEDED:

- 120 yards of 100% wool yarn
- Scissors
- Crochet hook or yarn needle
- Nylons or pantyhose

INSTRUCTIONS:

1. To get the ball started, wrap the yarn around three fingers about 10 times, and then pull the yarn off your fingers. Pinch this small yarn bundle between your fingers, and wrap 10 times around that bunch.
2. Wrap the yarn about 5–10 times in every direction to create a ball shape.
3. Once the yarn ball is a little bigger than a tennis ball, cut the yarn, and secure the end by pulling it through several layers of wrapped yarn with the use of a blunt-tip yarn needle or crochet hook. You could use your fingers, but it will be more difficult to get a strong hold.
4. Place the wool balls in a nylon, tying a knot in between each ball.
5. Place the balls along with other laundry in the washing machine, and wash on a hot/cold cycle. Dry the balls in the dryer on the hottest heat setting. The change in temperature helps the yarn to felt. You may need to do 3–4 wash cycles to get your balls to felt. You will know when it has felted if you can't pull individual strands of yarn when you run your finger across the ball.
6. To use, add 1–2 drops of essential oil to each ball, and add to a load of laundry when drying.

Have you heard of these nifty wool dryer balls that are a natural and better alternative to dryer sheets? Not only do these balls help soften and dry your clothes faster, but you can also add essential oils to give your laundry a fresh scent without the use of a dryer sheet! Because these dryer balls do not contain fabric softener, they can even be used with cloth diapers, microfiber cloths, and other fabrics that aren't supposed to be dried with dryer sheets.

CITRUS-SCENTED WAX MELTS

Time: 5–10 minutes active; 2–3 hours inactive   Difficulty: Easy

INGREDIENTS AND MATERIALS NEEDED:

- 2 oz. beeswax pellets
- 2 Tbsp. coconut oil
- 10 drops orange essential oil
- 5 drops tangerine essential oil
- 5 drops bergamot essential oil

INSTRUCTIONS:

1. Melt together the coconut oil and beeswax in a double boiler on the stove, stirring frequently. Once completely liquid, remove from heat.
2. Stir in the essential oil using a bamboo skewer.
3. Pour mixture into molds, and then set aside to cool.
4. Once cooled and solidified, you can remove the wax melts from the molds and use them in your candle warmer.
5. Enjoy the refreshing, citrusy scent!

CITRUS-SCENTED WAX MELTS

CRAFTS

ORANGE, TANGERINE, & BERGAMOT ESSENTIAL OILS

CLOTHESPIN CAR DIFFUSER

CRAFTS

YOUR CHOICE OF ESSENTIAL OIL

CLOTHESPIN CAR DIFFUSER

Time: 5 minutes active   Difficulty: Easy

INGREDIENTS AND MATERIALS NEEDED:

- Scissors
- Felt or diffuser scent pad
- Clothespin
- Decorations such as ribbon, buttons, charms, etc.
- Hot glue gun

INSTRUCTIONS:

1. Using scissors, cut the felt or diffuser pad to the width of the clothespin.
2. If desired, cut strips of ribbon to use as decorations on the clothespin.
3. Using a hot glue gun, glue the diffuser pad and any decorations to the clothespin.
4. To use, simply add 5–10 drops of essential oil to the diffuser pad or felt, and clip the clothespin onto any air vent. Turn the air on to begin diffusing.

CAR TRAVEL TIPS:

1. Diffusing invigorating oils such as peppermint, ylang ylang, lemon, basil, and rosemary in the car can help the driver stay alert while traveling.
2. Peppermint is also a good oil for alleviating occasional stomach discomfort.
3. While traveling during the summer months, especially when the car has been parked in the hot sun for a while, even a good air conditioner in the car doesn't always work fast enough to keep you cool. Several essential oils that have a cooling effect include peppermint, eucalyptus, melaleuca, lavender, Roman chamomile, and citrus oils. Diffuse these oils in the car.

PINE CONE OWL DIFFUSER

Time: **30 minutes active**   Difficulty: **Easy**

MATERIALS NEEDED:

- Pine cones
- Owl template (included in appendix)
- Felt
- Scissors
- Hot glue gun
- Essential oils

INSTRUCTIONS:

1. Gather pine cones of your desired sizes, and carefully rinse them off with warm water to get rid of any dirt. Set them on a towel to dry.
2. Photocopy the owl template, and cut out the pattern pieces. You may need to scale the template depending on the size of your pine cones. Trace the pattern pieces onto felt of your desired colors, and then cut out the felt.
3. Use the hot glue gun to attach the felt pieces to the pine cone: Glue the eye and beak pieces together, and then glue them to the front of the pine cone near the top. Glue a wing piece on each side of the pine cone, and glue the feet pieces to the bottom of the pine cone. Repeat for any additional pine cone diffusers you wish to make.
4. Once the glue has dried, your pine cone diffusers are ready to enjoy! Drop 2 or 3 drops of essential oil on the top of each pine cone, and enjoy the fragrance!

PINE CONE OWL DIFFUSER

CRAFTS

YOUR CHOICE OF ESSENTIAL OIL

NOTES:

CRAFTS FOR CHILDREN

SCENTED BUBBLES

Yield: 8 oz.   Time: 10 minutes active; 12–24 hours inactive   Difficulty: Easy

INGREDIENTS:

- 3/4 cup water (Distilled water works best, but tap water can be used as well.)
- 1/4 cup unscented dish soap
- 1 Tbsp. liquid glycerin
- 15–20 drops essential oil
- 8 oz. plastic bottle or several 4 oz. or 2 oz. plastic bottles.

INSTRUCTIONS:

1. In a small bowl or cup, mix together your desired essential oil or blend and the unscented dish soap. Allow to sit for a few minutes.
2. Add liquid glycerin, and mix together.
3. Add the soap and essential oil mixture to the water in a mixing bowl.
4. Stir the mixture carefully until everything is blended together (do not whisk or stir rapidly, or you'll end up making a lot of froth).
5. Pour mixture into an 8 oz. plastic bottle or into several 4 oz. or 2 oz. plastic bottles.
6. Allow mixture to sit for 12–24 hours to allow it to meld together.
7. To use the mixture, use standard bubble wands dipped into the bottles; or pour the mixture into a shallow bowl or pan, and use different shaped cookie cutters, pipe cleaners formed into loops, straws, or anything else you desire to blow the bubbles with.

SCENTED BUBBLES

YOUR CHOICE OF ESSENTIAL OIL

FUN SCENTED PLAY CLAY

CRAFTS FOR KIDS

YOUR CHOICE OF ESSENTIAL OIL

FUN SCENTED PLAY CLAY

Yield: **Makes 4 play clay balls**   Time: **15 minutes active**   Difficulty: **Easy**

INGREDIENTS AND MATERIALS NEEDED:

- 1 cup flour
- 1/4 cup salt
- 2 Tbsp. cream of tarter
- 1 Tbsp. oil
- 1 cup water
- Air-tight containers or bags for storage

INSTRUCTIONS:

1. Mix flour, salt, cream of tarter, oil, and water in a medium-sized pot until well blended.
2. While stirring continuously, cook the mixture in the pot over medium-low heat until it forms a thick dough that is no longer sticky (approximately 5 minutes). You can tell it is done when it no longer sticks to the sides of the pan but forms a clump of dough in the middle of the pan.
3. Remove the dough from the pan, and place on waxed paper. Allow to cool for about 5 minutes.
4. Divide the dough into four equal pieces.
5. For each of the four pieces of dough, add approximately 10 drops of different colored food coloring, and knead until the color is well blended into the dough.
6. Add approximately 8–10 drops of different essential oils or blends to each of the four pieces of dough, and knead for about 60 seconds. If you find the scent of the dough is not strong enough, add a few more drops of the essential oil or blend. (*Helpful hint: to make sure both the food coloring and the essential oil or blend stay in the dough and don't drip off, create a well in the top of the piece of dough with your finger, drop the coloring or oil in the well, fold the dough so it closes over the well opening, and then continue to knead the dough as normal.)
7. Store each piece of dough in a 4 oz. salve jar, zip-top bag, or other air-tight container.

EXTRA IDEA:

Try creating scents that match the color of the play clay you created. For example, try using peppermint oil for red or white, pine for green, wintergreen or birch (both have a rootbeer-like aroma) for brown, spruce for blue, orange oil for orange, and so forth.

AROMATHERAPY CLOUD DOUGH

Time: **5 minutes active**   Difficulty: **Easy**

INGREDIENTS AND MATERIALS NEEDED:

- 1/2 cup vegetable oil (or other cooking oil)
- 5 drops essential oil
- 6–8 drops food coloring (optional)
- 4 cups flour

INSTRUCTIONS:

1. In a glass bowl, mix vegetable oil, essential oil, and food coloring together until the color is distinct or until thoroughly combined.
2. Place flour in playing bin, and add oil mixture. Mix together until combined. You may need to use your hands.
3. You can store your Cloud Dough in an airtight container for up to a week.

NOTE: Some essential oils that would work well in this recipe and are safe to use with children are lavender, peppermint, ylang ylang, or Roman chamomile.

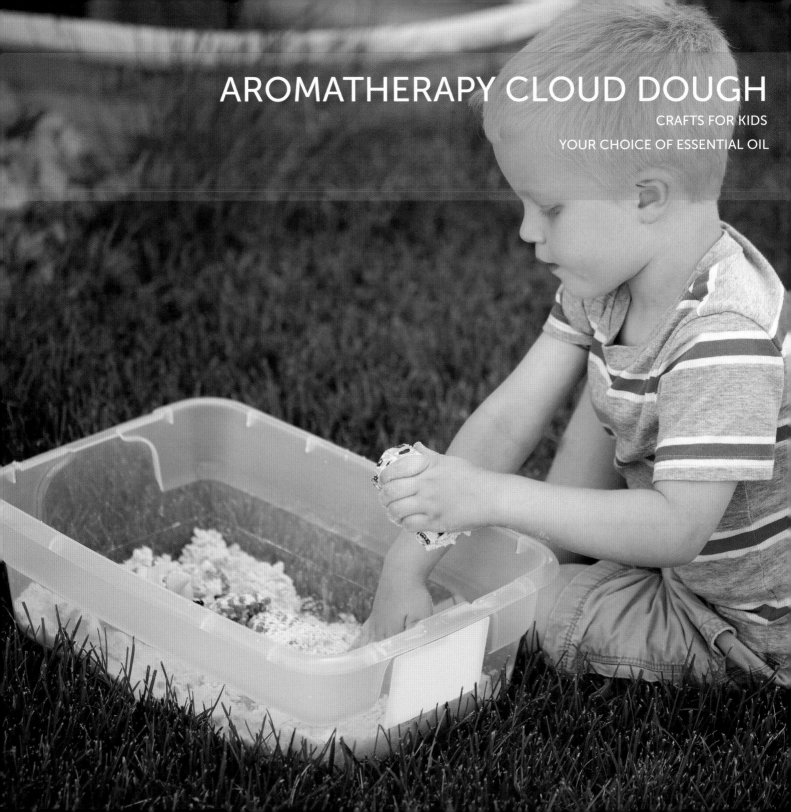

AROMATHERAPY CLOUD DOUGH

CRAFTS FOR KIDS

YOUR CHOICE OF ESSENTIAL OIL

ESSENTIAL OIL–SCENTED FINGER PAINTS

CRAFTS FOR KIDS

YOUR CHOICE OF ESSENTIAL OIL

ESSENTIAL OIL-SCENTED FINGER PAINTS

Yield: 2 cups paint   Time: 15–20 minutes active   Difficulty: Easy

INGREDIENTS AND MATERIALS NEEDED:

- 2 cups cold water
- 1 heaping Tbsp. cornstarch
- Plastic bottles
- Food coloring
- Essential oils

INSTRUCTIONS:

1. In a medium-size pot, whisk together cold water and cornstarch. Heat over medium heat, stirring often, until mixture thickens.
2. Remove from heat, and let cool.
3. Pour the mixture into plastic bottles, and add a different color of food coloring to each bottle, stirring in with a bamboo skewer, until you achieve your desired color.
4. Add a drop of essential oil to each bottle of paint, and stir in the essential oil with the bamboo skewer. Be sure to choose essential oils that are safe for children. It's fun to choose oil scents that go along with each color, and this also makes for a fun sensory experience. For example, mix a drop of lemon essential oil in with the yellow paint, a drop of peppermint essential oil in with the green paint, a drop of orange essential oil in with the orange paint, a drop of lavender essential oil in with the purple paint, etc.
5. Twist the lids onto your bottles, and your paint is ready to enjoy!

NOTES:

⊘ ◯ HOLIDAYS

ST. PATRICK'S DAY BEESWAX CANDLE
ESSENTIAL OIL BUNNY BUDDIES
PATRIOTIC FRUIT SHISH KEBABS
LEMON ESSENTIAL OIL FRUIT DIP
BEWITCHING CUPCAKES
CANDY CANE BATH SALTS
HOMEMADE VANILLA EXTRACT

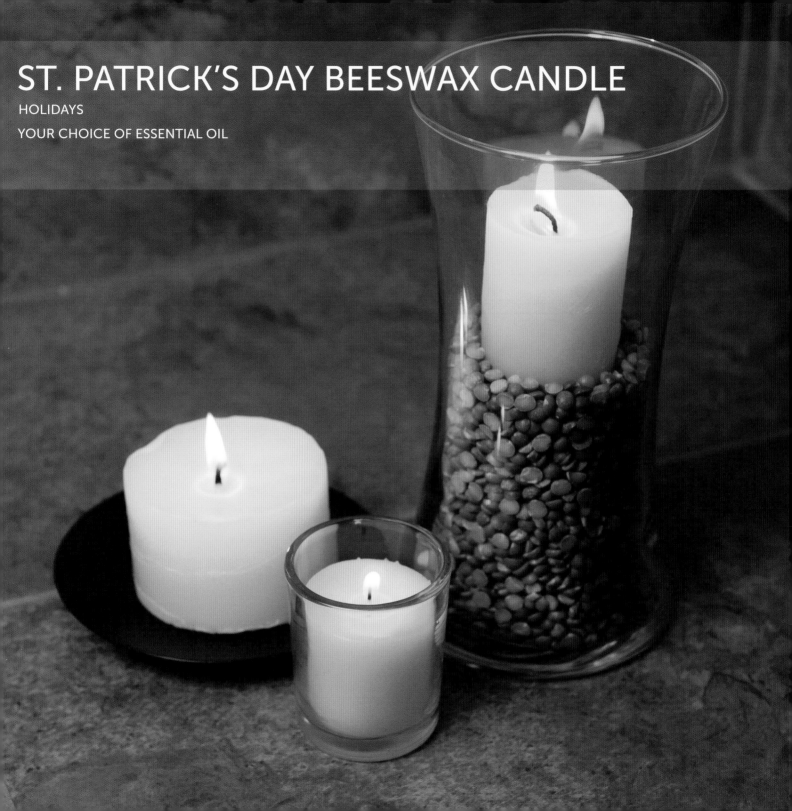

ST. PATRICK'S DAY BEESWAX CANDLE

HOLIDAYS

YOUR CHOICE OF ESSENTIAL OIL

ST. PATRICK'S DAY BEESWAX CANDLE

Time: 20 minutes active; 1 hour inactive   Difficulty: Easy

INGREDIENTS & MATERIALS NEEDED:

- Candle mold(s)
- Beeswax pellets
- Candle wick
- Essential oils
- Scotch tape
- Pencil(s)

INSTRUCTIONS:

1. Select your candle mold(s) based on the size and shape you want your candle(s) to be. You can purchase candle molds, or you can easily make your own out of common household items. Cardboard containers work best, just lightly spray the inside of the container first with cooking spray so that you will be able to remove your candle easily.
2. Fill your candle mold(s) with beeswax pellets a little higher than you want your finished candle (enough to compensate for the air space between the pellets). Pour the beeswax into a glass measuring cup, and place it in a sauce pan filled halfway with boiling water. Stir the beeswax occasionally until it is fully melted.
3. While your beeswax is melting, prepare your candle molds. Attach the candle wick to the bottom center of the mold with a piece of scotch tape, and then wrap the candle wick around a pencil and balance it on top of the mold, using additional tape to hold the pencil in place if necessary.
4. Once the beeswax is fully melted, remove the glass measuring cup from the stove, and add drops of essential oil until you reach your desired level of smell. Pour the beeswax into your candle mold(s), and then set it aside to dry.
5. When your candle is fully cooled and solid, remove the candle from the mold. If you made your own mold, you can just tear/cut the cardboard off. Trim the candle wick to your desired length.
6. To make your candle into a fun St. Patrick's Day decoration, fill a glass vase or candle holder partway with dried split peas, and then place your candle on top.

ESSENTIAL OIL BUNNY BUDDIES

Time: **1 hour active**   Difficulty: **Medium**

INGREDIENTS AND MATERIALS NEEDED:

- Flannel fabric (you can use another type of fabric, but it needs to be something that doesn't easily fray along the edges)
- Sewing scissor—both regular sewing scissors and pinking sheers if you have them
- Rice (approximately 1 cup per bunny you want to make)
- Essential oil (whatever scent you prefer; 1–2 drops per bunny you want to make)
- Sewing machine
- Needle and thread
- Ribbon
- Bunny Buddy Template (included in appendix)
- Straight pins

INSTRUCTIONS:

1. Fold your fabric in half with right sides out. Pin your Bunny Buddy Template to the fabric, and cut around the edges. If you are going to finish the edge with pinking sheers, cut about 1/8" away from the template edge. If you are going to just leave a straight edge, you can cut right along the edge of the template.
2. Unpin the template from your fabric, and bring your bunny cutout to the sewing machine, leaving the right sides out. You can pin the two pieces of fabric together to help keep them from slipping while you sew. Use your sewing machine to stitch around the outside of the bunny. If you are going to finish the edge with pinking sheers, sew about 1/4" in from the edge. If you are going to leave the edge straight, you can sew about 1/8" in from the edge. Leave an opening about 1 1/4" wide at the bottom of the bunny so that you will be able to get the rice in.
3. If you are going to finish the edge with the pinking sheers, do it now. Cut carefully along the edge of the bunny, being careful not to get too close to the stitched seam.
4. Pour your desired amount of rice (about 1 cup per bunny) into a glass measuring cup, and stir your desired amount of essential oil in with the rice (1–2 drops per bunny).
5. Using a funnel, or a rolled up piece of paper if you don't have a funnel, pour the rice into the bunny through the opening at the bottom. Shake the bunny a bit to make sure that the rice fills the whole bunny even after it settles a little.
6. Use a needle and thread to stitch closed the opening at the bottom of the bunny. You can use a sewing machine to do this part, but it is hard to stitch close to the edge with a sewing machine without the rice falling out.
7. Tie a piece of ribbon in a bow around the bunny's neck.
8. Take a moment to admire what a darling little bunny you just made!

ESSENTIAL OIL BUNNY BUDDIES

HOLIDAYS

YOUR CHOICE OF ESSENTIAL OIL

PATRIOTIC FRUIT SHISH KEBABS

Time: **15 minutes active**   Difficulty: **Easy**

INGREDIENTS AND MATERIALS NEEDED:

- Bananas
- Strawberries
- Blueberries
- Bamboo skewers

INSTRUCTIONS:

1. Cut bananas into thick slices, and remove stems from strawberries.
2. Thread the bananas, strawberries, and blueberries on the skewers, alternating in a red, white, and blue pattern.
3. Serve with fruit dip

LEMON ESSENTIAL OIL FRUIT DIP

Time: **10 minutes active**   Difficulty: **Easy**

INGREDIENTS:

- 1 package (8 oz.) cream cheese, softened
- 1 cup (8 oz.) sour cream
- 1/3 cup sugar
- 2 tsp. vanilla extract
- 3–4 drops of lemon essential oil

INSTRUCTIONS:

1. Mix together cream cheese, sour cream, sugar, vanilla, and lemon essential oil with an electric hand mixer until smooth.
2. Serve with your choice of fresh fruits or our Patriotic Fruit Shish Kebabs.

PATRIOTIC FRUIT SHISH KEBABS

HOLIDAYS

LEMON ESSENTIAL OIL

BEWITCHING CUPCAKES

HOLIDAYS

YOUR CHOICE OF ESSENTIAL OIL

BEWITCHING CUPCAKES WITH ESSENTIAL OIL FROSTING

Yield: 24 cupcakes   Time: 40 minutes active   Difficulty: Medium

INGREDIENTS:

- 1 package (3.5 oz.) instant vanilla pudding mix
- 1 cup milk
- 1 container (8 oz.) frozen whipped topping, thawed
- 1 tsp. homemade vanilla extract (see page 137)
- 1–3 drops of the food-safe essential oil of your choice
- Food coloring (if desired)
- 24 cupcakes, made with your favorite recipe
- 24 chocolate-flavored ice cream cones (or vanilla cones dipped in chocolate, if you choose)

INSTRUCTIONS:

1. In a medium-size bowl, whisk together pudding mix and milk until well combined.
2. Stir in whipped topping and vanilla extract.
3. Add essential oil of your choice.
4. Divide the frosting into separate bowls, and color each bowl of frosting with your desired food coloring.
5. Frost the cupcakes with the color of frosting you want for your base.
6. Using an alternate color of frosting, pipe a belt buckle (or other design of your choice) along the bottom of a chocolate cone. You can use a special frosting bag and piping tools if you have them, or you can use a zip-top bag with a small corner cut off. Hint: If you frosting seems too soft to frost properly, put it in the fridge for a few minutes to chill, and then try again.
7. Place the decorated ice cream cone on top of a frosted cupcake.
8. Continue until all of your cupcakes are decorated, and then enjoy your masterpiece!

CANDY CANE BATH SALTS

Time: **15 minutes active**   Difficulty: **Easy**

INGREDIENTS AND MATERIALS NEEDED:

- 16 oz. Epsom salts
- 1 Tbsp. baking soda
- 4 drops peppermint essential oil
- Red natural food dye
- 6 clear plastic tubes with silver lids (75 ml size)

INSTRUCTIONS:

1. Divide the Epsom salts in half between two mixing containers. Color one container of the Epsom salts red with the natural food dye.
2. Add 2 drops peppermint essential oil and 1/2 Tbsp. baking soda to each container, and stir.
3. Layer the different colors of bath salt alternately in each of the tubes to create a candy cane look. Do not shake.
4. These bath salts make a great holiday gift for friends, family, and neighbors.

HOMEMADE VANILLA EXTRACT
HOLIDAYS

HOMEMADE VANILLA EXTRACT

Yield: Thirty-five 4 oz. bottles   Time: 20 minutes active; 3 months inactive   Difficulty: Easy

The best thing about homemade vanilla is that if you leave the beans in the bottle, it just keeps getting better the longer you let it sit. When gifting this, make sure to leave 1–2 vanilla beans in every 4 oz. bottle so it not only looks authentic, but also so your friends can enjoy a richer vanilla flavor over time.

It takes about 12 weeks for the vanilla beans to infuse their flavor in the alcohol, so this is a great gift to make in advance. If you don't have enough time to let it sit for 12 weeks, just include a date on the label for when it can be used.

INGREDIENTS AND MATERIALS NEEDED:

- 60 vanilla beans (about 1/2 lb)
- 2 bottles of vodka or white rum (1.75 liter size)
- 5 canning jars (1 quart size)
- 4 oz. glass bottles (approximately 35 bottles)

INSTRUCTIONS:

1. Cut off the ends of the vanilla beans, and cut each bean lengthwise. Divide the vanilla beans evenly among the glass canning jars.
2. Pour the vodka or rum into the canning jars, covering the vanilla beans, and close tightly. Shake vigorously.
3. Place in a cool, dark place, and shake the bottles about once a week for a few months (about 12 weeks).
4. When ready to gift, carefully fill each 4 oz. glass bottle with vanilla extract, and secure the lids tightly. Include 1–2 vanilla beans in each bottle (you'll need to cut each bean in half to fit).
5. Add a label to the bottle, and include any instructions and the kind of vanilla. If it still needs to sit longer, include a date for when it can be used.

EXTRA IDEAS:
- Use a drop or two of homemade vanilla extract with cassia, cinnamon, peppermint, or orange essential oils in a cooking recipe or diffuser blend to add a wonderully unique twist.
- To spice up a gift of homemade vanilla extract, you can include your favorite recipe that uses vanilla extract and another ingredient in the recipe such as chocolate chips.

NOTES:

 # BODY CARE

- ALL-NATURAL MOISTURIZING LOTION
- SIMPLY NATURAL LIP BALM
- BERRY MINT LIP STAIN
- BROWN SUGAR LIP SCRUB
- LUXURIOUS BATH BOMBS
- DRY SHAMPOO
- LAVENDER LOTION BAR
- BABY WIPES
- COOLING ALOE VERA PEPPERMINT LOTION
- HOMEMADE FOAMING HAND SOAP
- EXFOLIATING FOOT OR BODY SCRUB
- FACIAL CLEANSING WIPES
- EYE MAKEUP REMOVER
- MAKEUP REMOVER
- NAIL POLISH REMOVER
- NAIL STRENGTHENING SERUM
- LUXURIOUS LAVENDER BUBBLE BATH
- HAND DEGREASER
- BASIC HAND WIPES
- AFTERSHAVE LOTION
- LAVENDER-SCENTED DEODORANT

ALL-NATURAL MOISTURIZING LOTION

Yield: 8 oz. of lotion   Time: 30 minutes active; 12 hours, 25 minutes inactive   Difficulty: Medium

INGREDIENTS AND MATERIALS NEEDED:

- 1/8 cup old fashioned oats
- 1/2 cup distilled water
- 1/4 cup jojoba oil or almond oil
  (olive oil would work too)
- 1/4 cup coconut oil
- 1 1/2 Tbsp. beeswax pellets
  (use more if you want a thicker lotion)
- 1/2 Tbsp. vitamin E oil (for its benefits to the
  skin as well as for preservation of the lotion)
- 1/2 Tbsp. raw honey
- 4–6 drops essential oil of your choice.
- Lotion bottle(s): We recommend a bottle with a lotion
  pump, such as an acrylic lotion pump
  bottle, since this recipe makes a thinner lotion.

INSTRUCTIONS:

1. Combine the old fashioned oats and distilled water. Cover, and let soak for 12 hours (starting this the night before works great). Distilled water is needed to inhibit mold growth. If you don't have distilled water, you can use regular tap water as long as you boil it and allow it to cool before mixing it with the oats.
2. After the oats have soaked for 12 hours, use a spatula to strain out the oatmeal water. This liquid should appear a little cloudy. If needed, use the spatula to squeeze the liquid from the oats. Set aside 1/4 cup of the oatmeal water. Discard or eat the oats.
3. Combine the jojoba oil, coconut oil, beeswax pellets, vitamin E oil, and honey in a glass bowl.
4. Place the glass bowl in the microwave or on the stovetop in a pan filled with an inch of simmering water (creating a double boiler). Heat until completely melted. The beeswax will take the longest, so make sure to use pellets or grate finely.

ALL-NATURAL MOISTURIZING LOTION

BODY CARE

YOUR CHOICE OF ESSENTIAL OIL

5. Once completely melted, pull the glass bowl out of the pan with a hot pad. Grab a towel, and fold it around the bottom of the glass bowl. Place the towel and glass bowl in the refrigerator to cool off for 10 minutes before placing in the freezer (towel and all), or just leave the bowl in the refrigerator for another 35 minutes until the mixture is soft and cool.

NOTE: Some glass dishes can break if the temperature change is too drastic, so use caution. Wrap a towel around and under the dish; then let it cool first in the fridge before placing it in the freezer. The towel keeps the glass from touching anything really cold.

6. Mix together the cooled oil mixture, 1/4 cup of oatmeal water, and 4–6 drops of essential oil with a handheld or stand electric mixer. Whip for a few minutes until thickened and lotion-looking.
7. Pour the lotion into a plastic bag. With scissors, cut off a corner of the bag just a tiny bit, and squeeze the lotion into an empty lotion bottle.

NOTE: Store this lotion at room temperature (75 degrees Fahrenheit) or less. If you know it will be hotter than 75 degrees, you can store it in the fridge to keep the oil and water from separating. However, if stored in the fridge, it may need to be brought back to room temperature before using in a pump bottle.

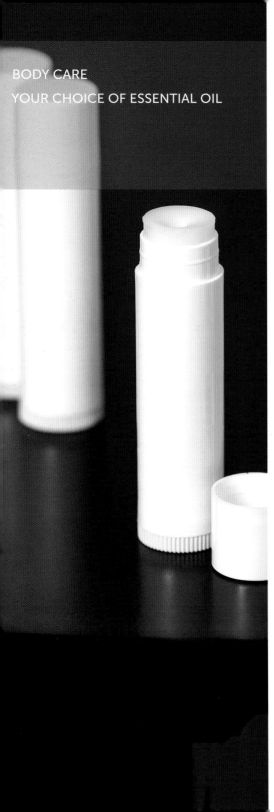

SIMPLY NATURAL LIP BALM

Yield: 8–12 lip balms   **Time:** 15 minutes active   **Difficulty:** Easy

INGREDIENTS:

- 6 grams (4 tsp.) beeswax pellets
- 10 grams (1 Tbsp.) cocoa butter
- 3 Tbsp. (1 ml) jojoba oil
- 10–20 drops essential oil (Some oils that work well with this recipe include lavender, peppermint [which can have a cooling effect], or a lemon-thyme blend [15 drops lemon and 3–5 drops thyme])
- Lip balm containers (12), lip gloss containers (8–10), or 1/4 oz. glass salve jars (8–10)

INSTRUCTIONS:

1. Using a kitchen scale, measure out the beeswax pellets and cocoa butter. Place them in a heat-proof glass measuring cup.
2. Melt the oils in the microwave or on the stovetop in a pan filled with an inch of simmering water (creating a double boiler). Heat until completely melted.
3. Add jojoba oil to the melted oils, and continue to heat until all the oil is incorporated.
4. Allow to cool for a minute, and then stir in essential oils.
5. Pour the mixture into your lip balm containers of choice. You may find it easier to use a small dropper or small funnel to transfer the mixture into the small containers without spilling on the side.
6. Allow mixture to cool and solidify before using.

BERRY MINT LIP STAIN

Yield: 1/4 oz.   Time: **10–15 minutes active**   Difficulty: **Easy**

INGREDIENTS:

- 3 blackberries
- 3 raspberries
- 1 small strawberry, stem removed
- 1/2 tsp. sweet almond oil
- 1 drop peppermint essential oil
- 1/4 oz. glass salve jar

INSTRUCTIONS:

1. Place berries in a heat-proof glass dish, and soften in the microwave or on the stovetop in a pan filled with an inch of simmering water (creating a double boiler).
2. Mash well with a fork. Mix in sweet almond oil and peppermint oil.
3. Strain mixture through a cheesecloth or coffee filter, and fill your container.
4. Place in fridge, and allow to cool completely before using. Store in fridge when not in use.
5. To use, simply dip your finger in the lip stain, and apply it to lips.
6. Wash fingers immediately to prevent staining.

NOTE: If you have dry or cracked lips, this stain can make those areas stand out. To avoid this, try exfoliating with our Brown Sugar Lip Scrub (next page) first.

BROWN SUGAR LIP SCRUB

Time: 3 minutes active   Difficulty: Easy

INGREDIENTS AND MATERIALS NEEDED:

- 3 Tbsp. brown sugar
- 1 Tbsp. coconut oil
- 1–2 drops peppermint essential oil
  or other desired essential oil
- 2 oz. glass salve jar

INSTRUCTIONS:

1. Mix together all ingredients, and transfer to a 2 oz. glass salve jar.
2. To use, place a small amount on the lips, and rub lips together for a couple minutes.
3. Finish by rinsing lips with water.

BROWN SUGAR LIP SCRUB

BODY CARE

PEPPERMINT ESSENTIAL OIL

LUXURIOUS BATH BOMBS

Yield: 6–9 bath bombs   Time: 20 minutes active; 12 hours inactive   Difficulty: Easy

INGREDIENTS AND MATERIALS NEEDED:

- 2/3 cup baking soda
- 1/2 cup cornstarch
- 1/3 cup Epsom salts
- 1/3 cup citric acid
- 2 tsp. water
- 2 tsp. coconut oil
- 10–20 drops of essential oil
- Spray bottle with water

INSTRUCTIONS:

1. Combine dry ingredients in a medium bowl and the wet ingredients in a small bowl.
2. Add the wet ingredients to the dry ingredients, and mix well with a whisk. The mixture will bubble just a bit and begin to clump together. After mixing a little with the whisk, put the whisk aside and work it with your fingers. Mix and blend the mixture until it is well combined and has the texture of mildly wet sand. It should clump together when you squeeze it with your fingers. If it is too dry, moisten it with the water in the spray bottle, one spritz at a time. You do not want the mixture too wet or it will not set up properly.
3. Press the mixture firmly into silicone soap molds or muffin tins lined with paper cups or plastic wrap (for easy removal). Let sit for 1–2 hours.
4. After the bath bombs are dry enough that they stick together, remove them from the molds or muffin tins (and paper cups), and let them sit on a fluffy towel overnight before using. If you live in a humid area, you may need to dry the bath bombs for 2 nights before they'll be set enough to gift or use.

EXTRA IDEAS
- Try using food coloring and dry herbs to decorate the bath bombs a little more.
- Try dividing the batch after mixing the dry ingredients to make bath bombs with different scents or colors. Work with one scent at a time. Mix in the appropriate amount of the wet ingredients, moisten with the spray bottle if necessary, and press firmly into the molds before starting the process over again with another scent.
- Try different essential oils for different purposes. For example, try making some relaxing bath bombs with soothing essential oils (e.g. lavender, ylang ylang, or Roman chamomile) or energizing bath bombs with invigorating essential oils (e.g. citrus oils, peppermint, eucalyptus, or rosemary).

LUXURIOUS BATH BOMBS

YOUR CHOICE OF ESSENTIAL OIL

DRY SHAMPOO

Time: 2 minutes active   Difficulty: Easy

INGREDIENTS AND MATERIALS NEEDED:

- 2 Tbsp. arrowroot powder
  (or for dark hair: 1 Tbsp. arrowroot
  powder + 1 Tbsp. cocoa powder)
- 1–3 drops essential oil(s)
- Salve jar

INSTRUCTIONS:

1. In a small bowl, mix together the arrowroot powder, cocoa powder (for dark hair), and essential oils. Transfer to salve jar.
2. To use, dab an old makeup brush into the powder; then tap the brush on the inside of the salve jar lid to shake off the excess powder. Lift up a small section of hair, and apply powder to the hair roots. Repeat with different sections of hair until powder has been applied to all the greasy areas of the hair. Leave for a few minutes before brushing out the excess powder.

NOTE: The ingredients in this dry shampoo are simple: arrowroot powder, cocoa powder (optional), and essential oils. The arrowroot powder absorbs the oil and leaves your hair looking clean. The cocoa powder also helps absorb oil, but it is mainly used to create a darker dry shampoo for those with darker hair. The essential oils are used for scent and to provide extra benefits for your hair.

Modern Essentials suggests the following oils for hair:

PROMOTES HEALTHY HAIR: clary sage, lavender, thyme, sandalwood, wintergreen, and Roman chamomile

BENEFITS OILY HAIR CONDITIONS: basil, cypress, thyme, lemon, and rosemary

SUPPORTS NORMAL HAIR GROWTH: thyme, lavender, rosemary, ylang ylang, cedarwood, clary sage, and geranium

When choosing which essential oils to use in your dry shampoo, pick 1–3 of the above oils or other oils that smell good to you, smell good together, and provide the benefits you need.

DRY SHAMPOO

BODY CARE

YOUR CHOICE OF ESSENTIAL OIL

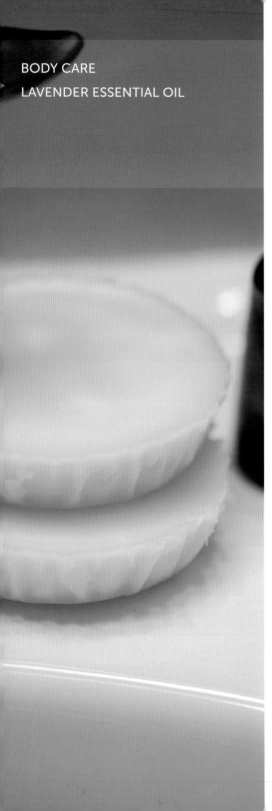

LAVENDER LOTION BARS

Yield: **4 bars** Time: **15 minutes active; 1 hour inactive** Difficulty: Eas

INGREDIENTS AND MATERIALS NEEDED:

- 4 muffin tin liners
- 1 muffin tin
- 1/4 cup coconut oil
- 1/4 cup shea butter
- 1/4 cup beeswax
- 10 drops lavender essential oil

INSTRUCTIONS:

1. Place muffin tin liners in muffin tin. Set aside.
2. Melt together the coconut oil, shea butter, and beeswax in a double boiler on the stove. Then remove from heat.
3. Stir in essential oil.
4. Pour mixture into prepared muffin tin.
5. Let cool completely.
6. Remove lotion bars from tin.
7. To use, just rub the bar across your skin, and then rub the lotion in with your hands.

BABY WIPES

Yield: **1 3/4 cups of solution**   Time: **5 minutes active**   Difficulty: **Easy**

INGREDIENTS AND MATERIALS NEEDED:

- 1 1/2 cups distilled water
- 2 Tbsp. fractionated coconut oil
- 2 Tbsp. witch hazel
- 6–8 drops vitamin E oil (2 capsules)
- 3–4 drops lavender essential oil
- 3–4 drops melaleuca (tea tree) essential oil
- 16 oz. jar or baby wipe container
- Dry bamboo wipes

INSTRUCTIONS:

1. Mix all ingredients in a 16 oz. jar or baby wipe container. Shake until well combined.
2. To use, shake the jar, and dip a bamboo wipe in the liquid. Squeeze out the extra liquid, and use to wipe the baby.
3. If you go through these fairly quickly, you can mix all the ingredients in a bowl and pour them over the bamboo wipes in the wipe container. However, due to the nature of using natural ingredients, mold may develop if the wipes are not used quickly.

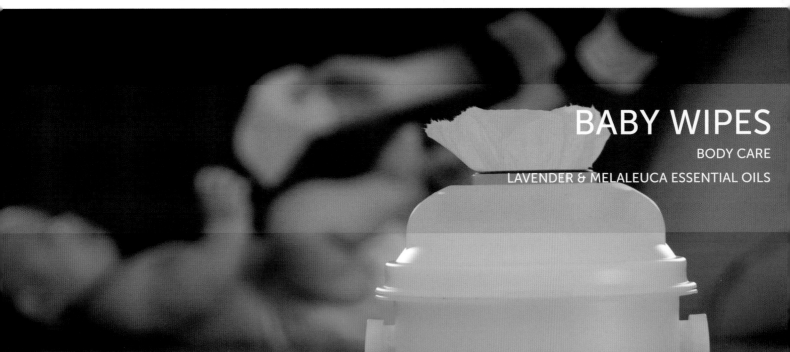

BABY WIPES
BODY CARE
LAVENDER & MELALEUCA ESSENTIAL OILS

COOLING ALOE VERA PEPPERMINT LOTION

BODY CARE

PEPPERMINT ESSENTIAL OIL

COOLING ALOE VERA PEPPERMINT LOTION

Yield: 1¼ cup   Time: 15 minutes active; 45 minutes inactive   Difficulty: Easy

INGREDIENTS:

- 1/4 cup beeswax pellets
- 1/2 cup extra-virgin coconut oil
- 1/2 cup aloe vera gel
- 10–20 drops peppermint essential oil
- 12 oz. jar

INSTRUCTIONS:

1. Place the beeswax in a medium-size glass dish. Melt in the microwave or on the stovetop in a pan filled with an inch of simmering water (creating a double boiler). Heat until almost completely melted.
2. Add the coconut oil to the beeswax, and finish melting.
3. Remove from the heat, and allow to cool to room temperature (about an hour).

NOTE: You can wrap the glass dish in a towel and place it in the refrigerator (35–45 minutes) or freezer (10–15 minutes) to speed up the cooling process.

NOTE: Some glass dishes can break if the temperature change is too drastic. Use caution. Wrap a towel around and under the dish; then let it cool first in the fridge before placing it in the freezer. The towel keeps the glass from touching anything really cold.

4. Once cool, add the aloe vera gel and peppermint essential oil, and mix together with a handheld or stand electric mixer for a few minutes until well incorporated and fluffy.
5. Place lotion in a 12 oz. PET jar or other wide-mouth jar.
6. Store at room temperature (65–72 degrees) or in a refrigerator. Coconut oil turns to a liquid state at 76 degrees Fahrenheit, and your lotion will become very runny.

Are you feeling hot this summer? Try this lotion recipe to cool off after being in the heat—you will love how it feels!

HOMEMADE FOAMING HAND SOAP

Yield: **8 oz.**   Time: **2 minutes active**   Difficulty: **Easy**

INGREDIENTS AND MATERIALS NEEDED:

- 1/4–1/3 cup unscented liquid Castile soap
- 2/3 cup water (distilled or boiled is best, but tap water will also work)
- 10–12 drops essential oil of your choice
- 8 oz. bottle with foamer pump

INSTRUCTIONS:

Simply mix the liquid Castile soap and essential oil in the foamer bottle; then fill the remainder of the bottle with water (only fill to about an inch and a half from the top to save room for the foamer pump), and screw the lid on. Feel free to wash your hands immediately and enjoy your homemade foaming soap.

EXTRA IDEA
- Turn this into a face wash by only using 1/4 cup liquid Castile soap, adding 5 drops melaleuca essential oil, and filling the rest up with water.

HOMEMADE FOAMING HAND SOAP

BODY CARE

YOUR CHOICE OF ESSENTIAL OIL

EXFOLIATING FOOT OR BODY SCRUB

BODY CARE

YOUR CHOICE OF ESSENTIAL OIL

EXFOLIATING FOOT OR BODY SCRUB

Yield: 4 oz. of scrub   Time: 5 minutes active   Difficulty: Easy

INGREDIENTS AND MATERIALS NEEDED:

- 1/4 cup Epsom salt or another exfoliating agent
  (You can also use coarse sea salt, fine sea salt, raw sugar,
  brown sugar, table salt, or white sugar. The coarser the salt
  is, the more exfoliating it will be.)
- 1/4 cup sweet almond oil
- 2 capsules or 6–8 drops of vitamin E (optional)
  (This can be found as either capsules or liquid in most
  health, grocery, and drug stores. Besides being an
  antioxidant, vitamin E is also a natural preservative.)
- 10–20 drops of essential oil(s)
- Container to store your scrub

INSTRUCTIONS:

1. Pour all ingredients into a bowl, and mix together.
2. Pour the mixture into a 4 oz. salve container or small wide-mouth jar.
3. To use the scrub, place a small amount in the palm, and scrub over moistened skin. Rinse off in a shower or tub. (Note: the oils in this scrub can make the floor of the bathtub or shower rather slippery, so use extreme caution while rinsing off so you don't fall.)

EXTRA IDEAS
- Use ultramarine powders or other natural powders and oil-soluble colorants to color your scrubs.
- Try using different coarsenesses of salt or sugar to create progressively smoother scrubs (i.e. a coarse "buffing" scrub, followed by a fine "polishing" scrub) with different essential oils to help relax in each scrub.
- Try combining two or more exfoliating agents to get a different feel for your scrub.

NOTE: While salt works very well as an exfoliating agent, it can sting if it gets into open cuts or sores, so be sure to either warn recipients to only use on unbroken skin, or use sugar as your exfoliator instead.

FACIAL WIPES

BODY CARE

LAVENDER, LEMON, & MELALEUCA

ESSENTIAL OILS

FACIAL CLEANSING WIPES

Yield: **1 cup of solution**   Time: **5 minutes active**   Difficulty: **Easy**

INGREDIENTS AND MATERIALS NEEDED:

- 3/4 cup very warm distilled water
- 1/2 Tbsp. coconut oil
- 1/2 tsp. rubbing alcohol (for emulsion)
- 3–4 drops vitamin E oil (1 capsule)
- 2 drops lavender essential oil
- 2 drops lemon essential oil
- 2 drops melaleuca (tea tree) essential oil
- 12 oz. jar
- Dry bamboo wipes

INSTRUCTIONS:

1. Shake or whisk all ingredients together in the jar until well combined. The warm water should melt the coconut oil, and the rubbing alcohol should help with the emulsion process.
2. To use, shake the jar, and dip a bamboo wipe in the liquid. Squeeze out extra liquid, and wipe face.

EYE MAKEUP REMOVER

Yield: 1/4 cup of solution   Time: 5 minutes active   Difficulty: Easy

INGREDIENTS AND MATERIALS NEEDED:

- 1 part olive oil
- 1 part witch hazel
- 1 part water
- 3–4 drops vitamin E oil (1 capsule)
- 2 oz. glass bottle with lid
- Dry bamboo wipes

INSTRUCTIONS:

1. Mix all ingredients in the 2 oz. bottle.
2. To use, shake the bottle, and dab the mixture on a dry bamboo wipe. Wipe over face and closed eyes.

MAKEUP REMOVER

Yield: 1/4 cup of solution   Time: 2 minutes active   Difficulty: Easy

INGREDIENTS AND MATERIALS NEEDED:

- 3 Tbsp. coconut oil
- 3–4 drops vitamin E oil (1 capsule)
- 2 oz. salve jar
- Dry bamboo wipes

INSTRUCTIONS:

1. Mix all ingredients in a 2 oz. salve jar.
2. To use, dip a bamboo wipe in the coconut oil mixture, wring it out, and then wipe over closed eyes or face. This also works great for fixing mistakes while applying makeup.

NAIL POLISH REMOVER

Time: **2 minutes active**   Difficulty: **Easy**

INGREDIENTS AND MATERIALS NEEDED:

- 5 drops lemon essential oil
- 3 drops orange essential oil
- 3 drops grapefruit essential oil
- White vinegar or rubbing alcohol
- 2 oz. glass bottle with black lid

INSTRUCTIONS:

1. Add essential oil(s) to the glass bottle. Fill the remainder of the bottle with white vinegar or rubbing alcohol. Screw the lid on, and shake to combine.
2. To use; simply dab some polish remover on a cotton ball. Rub over nail polish to remove.

NAIL STRENGTHENING SERUM

Time: **2 minutes active**   Difficulty: **Easy**

INGREDIENTS AND MATERIALS NEEDED:

- 25–30 drops of essential oil
- Fractionated coconut oil
- 2 oz. glass bottle with black lid

INSTRUCTIONS:

1. Add essential oil(s) to the glass bottle. Fill the remainder of the bottle with fractionated coconut oil. Screw the lid on, and shake to combine.
2. To use, simply dab some of the serum on a cotton ball or washcloth, and rub over nails to soften cuticles and strengthen nails.

THE FOLLOWING OILS HELP SUPPORT HEALTHY NAILS:
lemon, frankincense, myrrh, Invigorating Blend, eucalyptus, lavender, grapefruit, and rosemary essential oil

NAIL CARE KIT

LEMON, ORANGE, AND GRAPEFRUIT ESSENTIAL OILS

LUXURIOUS LAVENDER BUBBLE BATH

BODY CARE

LAVENDER ESSENTIAL OIL

LUXURIOUS LAVENDER BUBBLE BATH

Yield: 8 oz.   Time: 5 minutes active   Difficulty: Easy

INGREDIENTS AND MATERIALS NEEDED:

- 1/2 cup unscented dish soap
- 1/8 cup water
- 1/3 cup liquid glycerin
- 3 drops lavender essential oil
- 8 oz. plastic bottle

INSTRUCTIONS:

1. Stir together all ingredients in a glass liquid measuring cup or other glass dish, and then pour into an 8 oz. plastic bottle.
2. Finish by treating yourself to a luxurious lavender bubble bath!

At the end of a long day at work or with the kids, there is nothing quite like a warm, relaxing bubble bath to help you unwind. This luxurious bubble bath is easy to make and incorporates the benefits of pure, therapeutic-grade essential oils.

HAND DEGREASER

Yield: 1/4 cup   Time: 2 minutes active   Difficulty: Easy

INGREDIENTS AND MATERIALS NEEDED:

- 2 Tbsp. olive oil
- 2 Tbsp. Epsom salt (or other salt)
- 4–6 drops lemon essential oil
- 2 oz. glass bottle or salve jar

INSTRUCTIONS:

1. Mix all ingredients together in a 2 oz. glass bottle or salve jar.
2. To use, shake bottle to mix ingredients, dump out a little on hands, and rub hands together.

BASIC HAND WIPES

Yield: 3/4 cup of solution   Time: 5 minutes active   Difficulty: Easy

---

INGREDIENTS AND MATERIALS NEEDED:

- 1/2 Tbsp. liquid soap base such as Castile soap
- 1/2 Tbsp. carrier oil (such as olive oil or fractionated coconut oil, etc.)
- 3–5 drops essential oil of your choice
- 1/2 cup distilled water
- 10–20 bamboo wipes or paper towels
- Zip-top bag or small wipes container

INSTRUCTIONS:

1. Mix everything but water in a small bowl until well combined; then add water, and mix together (avoid making bubbles). Place 10–20 bamboo wipes in a zip-top bag, and pour the mixture over the wipes. Seal the bag, and let the liquid soak into the wipes.
2. To use, just pull a wipe from the bag, ring out any excess liquid, and wipe hands.

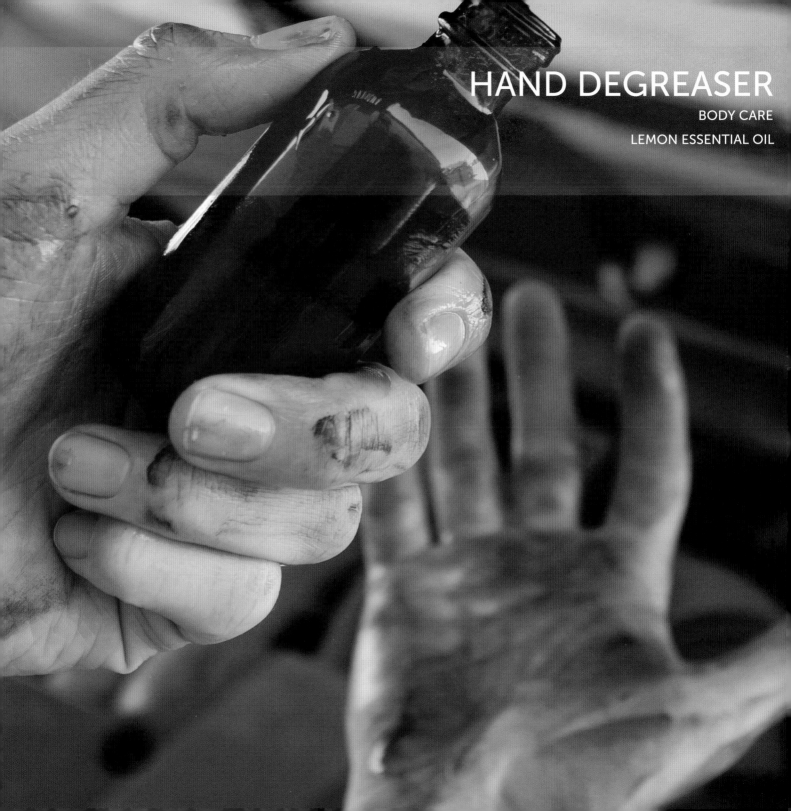

HAND DEGREASER
BODY CARE
LEMON ESSENTIAL OIL

AFTERSHAVE LOTION

BODY CARE

YOUR CHOICE OF ESSENTIAL OIL

AFTERSHAVE LOTION

Time: 15 minutes active   Difficulty: Easy

INGREDIENTS AND MATERIALS NEEDED:

- 4 tsp. beeswax pellets
- 1/3 cup coconut oil or grape seed oil (Note: grape seed oil is a great choice because it is great for skin, but it does have a scent. So if you don't mind the scent, grape seed oil is the best choice for aftershave.)
- 1/2–1 tsp. vitamin E oil (about 40 drops)
- 7 Tbsp. aloe vera gel (juice can substitute)
- 4 Tbsp. witch hazel
- 1/2 tsp. vegetable glycerin
- 20 drops essential oils of choice
- 4 oz. blue glass bottle with pump top

INSTRUCTIONS:

1. Combine the beeswax, coconut oil or grape seed oil, and vitamin E oil in a glass bowl.
2. Melt the oils in the microwave or on the stovetop in a pan filled with an inch of simmering water (creating a double boiler). Heat until completely melted. The beeswax will take the longest, so make sure to use pellets or grate finely. Remove from heat once completely melted.
3. In a separate glass bowl, mix together the aloe vera gel, witch hazel, and vegetable glycerin.
4. Whip the oil mixture with a handheld or stand electric mixer for a few seconds before slowly pouring the aloe vera gel mixture into the oil mixture. Add essential oils, and whip for a few minutes until thickened and lotion-looking.
5. Pour the lotion into a plastic bag. With scissors, cut off a corner of the bag just a tiny bit. Squeeze the lotion into the 4 oz. blue glass bottle, and screw on the pump top.

ALL-NATURAL LAVENDER-SCENTED DEODORANT

Yield: 2.65 oz.   Time: 30 minutes active   Difficulty: Easy

INGREDIENTS:

- 3 Tbsp. coconut oil
- 1 Tbsp. beeswax pellets
- 1/4 cup cornstarch
- 1/4 cup baking soda
- 1 vitamin E capsule (4–6 drops)
- 5 drops melaleuca essential oil
- 5 drops lavender essential oil
- 1 empty 2.65 oz. deodorant container

INSTRUCTIONS:

1. Combine coconut oil and beeswax pellets in a heat-proof glass bowl or glass measuring cup.
2. Place bowl or measuring cup in a saucepan filled with an inch of water. Heat mixture over medium heat, stirring occasionally, until completely melted.
3. Stir in cornstarch, baking soda, and the oil from one vitamin E capsule.
4. Remove from heat, and add essential oils.
5. Quickly pour mixture into an empty deodorant container.
6. Wait for mixture to harden and cool completely, and then start enjoying your all-natural essential oil deodorant!

Do you often find yourself in the deodorant aisle at the store for long periods of time reading ingredient labels and trying to find anything with ingredient names you actually recognize and without ingredients you know to be harmful? The best way to be sure that your deodorant is completely natural is to make it yourself!

ALL-NATURAL DEODORANT

BODY CARE

LAVENDER & MELALEUCA ESSENTIAL OILS

NOTES:

⊘ ⬭ CLEANING

CITRUS GARBAGE DISPOSAL FRESHENERS

DISHWASHER CLEANER

AIR FRESHENING SPRAY

ALL PURPOSE CLEANER (CASTILE SOAP)

ALL PURPOSE CLEANER (VINEGAR)

DEODORIZING TOILET SPRAY

LENS/SCREEN CLEANER WIPES

DRYER SHEETS

STREAK-FREE MIRROR/GLASS CLEANER

DUSTING SPRAY/WOOD
    FURNITURE CLEANER

CLEANING/ DISINFECTING WIPES

CITRUS GARBAGE DISPOSAL REFRESHERS

BODY CARE

LEMON & LIME ESSENTIAL OILS

CITRUS GARBAGE DISPOSAL REFRESHERS

Yield: Makes 16 half rounds   Time: 10 minutes active; 12 hours inactive   Difficulty: Easy

---

INGREDIENTS:

- 3/4 cup baking soda
- 1/2 cup salt
- 1 Tbsp. liquid dish soap or Castile soap
- Zest from 1 lime (optional)
- Juice from 1 lime or lemon
- 3–5 drops lime essential oil
- 8–10 drops lemon essential oil

INSTRUCTIONS:

1. Mix the baking soda and salt together in a bowl.
2. Stir in the liquid dish soap, lime zest, lime juice, and essential oils. Mix together with hands. The mixture should be a wet sand consistency; if it is not, add a little water until it becomes the right consistency.
3. Use a tablespoon to mold the disposal fresheners, and then place them on a baking sheet covered with parchment paper.
4. Leave the fresheners to dry overnight, and then place them in a glass jar to store.

When using the disposal fresheners, first place 3–4 ice cubes in the disposal; grind with cold water running to clear the disposal and sharpen the grinders. Then place 1–2 citrus refreshers in the disposal, and let them sit for a couple minutes before grinding with the water running.

DISHWASHER CLEANER

Time: 15–20 minutes active; 2 hours inactive   Difficulty: Easy

INGREDIENTS AND MATERIALS NEEDED:

- A washcloth
- A bowl of warm soapy water
- An old toothbrush
- A dishwasher-safe dish or container
- 2 cups of white distilled vinegar
- 7–10 drops of lemon essential oil

INSTRUCTIONS:

1. Remove the lower rack from your dishwasher.
2. Use a washcloth to wipe out any lose food or scum from the bottom of the dishwasher.
3. Use an old toothbrush and warm soapy water to clean around the seal and the edges of the dishwasher and the dishwasher door (anywhere the door covers when it is closed). Give the bottom of the dishwasher a quick scrub as well to loosen the scum up a bit.
4. Use the washcloth to wipe out any additional dirt you may have loosened up.
5. Fill a dishwasher-safe dish or container with 2 cups of white distilled vinegar.
6. Add 7–10 drops of lemon essential oil to the vinegar.
7. Place the container holding the vinegar and essential oil in the top rack of your dishwasher.
8. Close the dishwasher door, and select the hottest dishwasher cycle. Run the dishwasher empty for a full cycle.
9. Open your dishwasher, and be amazed at how much cleaner it looks and how wonderful it smells!

AIR FRESHENING SPRAY

Time: **3 minutes active**   Difficulty: **Easy**

INGREDIENTS:

- 1 tsp. liquid vegetable glycerin
- 10–15 drops essential oils
- 1/4 cup distilled water
- 2 oz. glass spray bottle

INSTRUCTIONS:

1. Place the glycerin and essential oils in the glass spray bottle. Swirl the bottle to mix the liquid.
2. Fill the rest of the bottle with distilled water, and shake to incorporate.
3. To use, simply spray around the room.

This Air Freshening Spray is a great way to help the air smell good without the harmful chemicals found in many commercial sprays. Another benefit to making your own spray is that you get to choose exactly what smell you want! We included a few essential oil blend suggestions to help you get started on the following page.

CLEAN & FRESH

 +  +

| 4 drops lemon essential oil | 4 drops lime essential oil | 2 drops rosemary essential oil |

CALMING

 +  +

| 10 drops lavender essential oil | 4 drops Roman chamomile essential oil | 1 drop frankincense essential oil |

FRESH FLORAL

 + +

| 6 drops lavender essential oil | 4 drops geranium essential oil | 2 drops Roman chamomile essential oil |

CITRUS SPICE

 + +  +

| 4 drops lemon essential oil | 5 drops orange essential oil | 3 drops grapefruit essential oil | 2 drops clove essential oil |

ALL-PURPOSE CLEANER (WITH CASTILE SOAP)

Yield: 8 oz.   Time: 3 minutes active   Difficulty: Easy

INGREDIENTS:

- 2 tsp. unscented Castile soap
- 15–20 drops disinfecting essential oil(s)
- 1 cup water
- 8 oz. glass spray bottle

Modern Essentials recommends the following oils to be used to cleanse and purify surfaces: Protective Blend, lemon, Cleansing Blend, melaleuca, lime, cinnamon, thyme, and peppermint.

INSTRUCTIONS:

1. Pour Castile soap and essential oils into the glass bottle.
2. Swish mixture to combine.
3. Fill the rest of the bottle with water. Screw on the spray top, and shake to combine.
4. Shake before using.
5. Use to clean; then spray on a vinegar-water solution after to clean away any soap scum.

ALTERNATE ALL-PURPOSE CLEANER (WITH VINEGAR)

Yield: 8 oz.   Time: 2 minutes active   Difficulty: Easy

INGREDIENTS:

- 15–20 drops disinfecting essential oil(s)
- 1/2 cup white vinegar
- 1/2 cup water
- 8 oz. glass spray bottle

INSTRUCTIONS:

1. Drop essential oils into the glass bottle.
2. Add vinegar, and then fill the rest of the bottle with water.
3. Screw on the spray top, and shake to combine.
4. Shake before using.

ALL-PURPOSE CLEANER

CLEANING

YOUR CHOICE OF ESSENTIAL OIL

DEODORIZING TOILET SPRAY

Time: **3 minutes active**   Difficulty: **Easy**

INGREDIENTS:

- 1 tsp. liquid vegetable glycerin
- 1 tsp. rubbing alcohol
- 10–15 drops essential oil
- 1/4 cup water
- 2 drops food coloring (optional)
- 2 oz. glass spray bottle

INSTRUCTIONS:

1. Place glycerin, alcohol, and essential oils in the glass spray bottle. Screw lid on, and shake to combine.
2. Unscrew the lid, and add the water and food coloring. Place the spray top on the bottle again, and shake to combine.
3. To use, shake the bottle, and then spray a few times in the toilet before you do your business.

"All living things eat, so everyone poops!"
—*Everyone Poops* by Taro Gomi

Now that we are clear on that subject, let's talk about how to make it a pleasant experience! This Deodorizing Toilet Spray is meant to be used before the elimination process begins. When you spray it in the toilet, the ingredients create a film on top of the water. This creates a barrier and fresh scent on top of the water so as you do your business it traps the smell beneath the surface. The food coloring is optional but is a nice reassurance that it works.

SOME GREAT ESSENTIAL OIL BLEND RECIPES FOR A TOILET SPRAY INCLUDE THE FOLLOWING:

SWEET CITRUS

 +  +

5 drops lemongrass
essential oil

5 drops bergamot
essential oil

5 drops grapefruit
essential oil

OCEAN BREEZE

 + 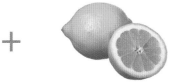 +

5 drops cedarwood
essential oil

4 drops lemon
essential oil

2 drops rosemary
essential oil

HERBAL BLISS

 +  +  +

4 drops lavender
essential oil

4 drops peppermint
essential oil

4 drops rosemary
essential oil

2 drops melaleuca
essential oil

LENS/SCREEN CLEANER

CLEANING

LEMON ESSENTIAL OIL

LENS/SCREEN CLEANER

Yield: 15 ml of solution   Time: 2 minutes active   Difficulty: Easy

INGREDIENTS AND MATERIALS NEEDED:

- 1 part white vinegar
- 1 part distilled water
- 1–2 drops lemon essential oil
- 15 ml glass bottle with spray top (can use an empty lemon essential oil bottle)

Do not use on plastic surfaces, as the lemon essential oil may harm the plastic!

INSTRUCTIONS:

1. Mix all ingredients in a 15 ml spray bottle.
2. To use, spray mixture on a dry soft cloth, and then wipe lens or screen.

DRYER SHEETS

Yield: 1/4 cup of solution   Time: 2 minutes active   Difficulty: Easy

INGREDIENTS AND MATERIALS NEEDED:

- 20 drops of your favorite essential oil
- Enough white vinegar to fill the rest of the bottle
- 2 oz. glass bottle with lid
- Safety pin(s) to reduce static (optional)

INSTRUCTIONS:

1. Mix essential oil and vinegar in a 2 oz. glass bottle with lid.
2. To use, dab mixture on a reusable wipe or cloth, and place the sheet in the dryer.
3. Add a safety pin or two to the sheet to reduce static.

STREAK-FREE MIRROR/GLASS CLEANER

Yield: **8 oz.**   Time: **3 minutes active**   Difficulty: **Easy**

INGREDIENTS:

- 2 Tbsp. white vinegar
- 2 Tbsp. rubbing alcohol
- 1 1/2 tsp. cornstarch (this is what makes it streak-free!)
- 8–10 drops citrus essential oil (lemon, lime, grapefruit, etc.)
- 3/4 cup water
- 8 oz. glass spray bottle

INSTRUCTIONS:

1. Mix together all ingredients except water in a spray bottle. Screw on the spray top, and shake to combine.
2. Unscrew the spray top, and fill the rest of the bottle with water. Screw on the spray top, and once again shake to combine.

STREAK-FREE MIRROR/GLASS CLEANER

CLEANING

CITRUS ESSENTIAL OIL

STREAK-FREE
MIRROR/GLASS
CLEANER

DUSTING SPRAY/WOOD FURNITURE CLEANER

CLEANING

LEMON & WHITE FIR ESSENTIAL OILS

DUSTING SPRAY/WOOD FURNITURE CLEANER

Yield: **8 oz.**   Time: **2 minutes active**   Difficulty: **Easy**

INGREDIENTS:

- 1 tsp. olive oil
- 5–10 drops essential oil
  (lemon or white fir are commonly used)
- 3 Tbsp. white vinegar
- 3/4 cup water
- 8 oz. glass spray bottle

INSTRUCTIONS:

1. Mix all ingredients together except water in a spray bottle. Swish mixture to combine.
2. Fill the rest of the bottle with water. Screw on the spray top, and shake to combine.
3. Shake before using.

CLEANING/DISINFECTING WIPES

Yield: **1 1/2 cups of solution**   Time: **5 minutes active**   Difficulty: **Easy**

INGREDIENTS:

- 3/4 cup distilled water
- 3/4 cup white vinegar
- 20–25 drops disinfecting oil(s)
- 16 oz. glass jar (a pint size canning jar works well)

INSTRUCTIONS:

1. Mix all ingredients together in a glass jar.
2. To use, dip a clean cloth in the liquid. Squeeze out extra liquid, and wipe the desired surface.

NOTES:

🖐 🌀 💧 MAKE & TAKE CLASS IDEAS

SPA NIGHT
AROMATHERAPY CLAY JEWELRY
NATURAL CLEANING SPRAYS
HOT CHOCOLATE SOCIAL
WINTER TIME PREP

SPA NIGHT

MAKE & TAKE CLASS IDEAS

PEPPERMINT & LAVENDER ESSENTIAL OILS

Have you been looking for a creative idea for your next essential oils class? How about a fun and relaxing spa night! Pull out the nail polish, chick flicks, and popcorn, and invite all your girlfriends over for a night of pampering, laughs, and relaxation. This is a great way to introduce your friends to essential oils in a fun and non-threatening environment. Below are a couple of fun recipes that you can use as part of your spa night.

AROMATIC PEPPERMINT FACIAL MASK

INGREDIENTS:
- 1 egg
- 1 tsp. jojoba oil
- 2–3 drops peppermint essential oil)

INSTRUCTIONS:
1. Beat egg with a whisk or a fork, and then mix in jojoba oil and essential oil.
2. Use fingers to apply mixture to face, avoiding the eye area.
3. Leave mask on for 10–15 minutes; then rinse face with cool water, and pat dry with a clean towel.

RELAXING LAVENDER FOOT OR HAND BATH

INGREDIENTS:
- Large basin for soaking feet or hands
- Warm water
- 1 tsp. powdered milk
- 3–5 drops lavender essential oil

INSTRUCTIONS:
1. Fill a basin big enough for hands or feet with warm water.
2. In a small glass dish, mix powdered milk and essential oil. Add powdered milk mixture to water basin, and stir in.
3. Soak feet or hands in basin for 10–15 minutes, or as long as desired.

CLASS IDEA: MAKE & TAKE AROMATHERAPY CLAY JEWELRY

Time: 30–45 minutes active; 24–72 hours inactive   **Difficulty:** Easy

Have you ever wanted to try making your own aromatherapy clay jewelry? When you make your own, you can customize it however you wish. The downside of making your own jewelry is that if you are only wanting to make one or two pieces, the cost for the materials may be more than the cost of buying the finished product. So, here's a fun idea that can help minimize the cost and allow you to make your own jewelry: host an essential oil jewelry make & take class!

Simply invite a few oil-loving friends or even potential oil lovers over for a fun night making clay jewelry. Have them bring a stamp or two; and if you are looking to share the costs, you can even ask them to bring a dollar or two for materials.

If you are inviting people who are new to essential oils, you may want to consider preparing a very short lesson about what essential oils are, how they are beneficial when used aromatically, and why aromatherapy jewelry is a great way to achieve these benefits. Present your lesson in the beginning before showing everyone the materials and how to make the jewelry. Then spend the rest of the time making clay pendants and beads, answering questions about essential oils, or simply enjoying the company of friends!

If you are doing this as a class or group activity, just follow steps 1–6 in the recipe on the next page (until they need to air dry); and then let them take their pendants home and finish them on their own.

The best thing about making your own clay jewelry is that you can make something that is your style, in whatever color you wish, and with whatever design you desire. You can even make something a boy would love to carry around or have in his room! And, you aren't limited to just jewelry. Even though necklace pendants are pretty popular, you can make charm bracelets, earrings, keychain pendants, car air fresheners, bathroom diffusers, etc. The possibilities are endless, so the hardest part is deciding what to make!

AROMATHERAPY CLAY JEWELRY

MAKE & TAKE CLASS IDEAS

YOUR CHOICE OF ESSENTIAL OIL

INGREDIENTS AND MATERIALS NEEDED:

- Air-dry white or terra-cotta clay (The Crayola Air-Dry brand works well.)
- Food coloring (optional; used for dying the white clay any color you desire)
- Rolling pin
- Cutout object
- Chopstick or shish kebab stick (This is used to make a hole for the cord. It needs to be big enough to fit 2 strands of string through.)
- Wax paper
- Sand paper (optional)
- Paints (optional)
- Ribbon, string, cord, or other jewelry-making materials
- Essential oil(s)

1 Take a lump of clay and rub in hands until soft and pliable. If you would like to dye the clay, do it now.

Helpful Hint: You can make beads out of the excess clay.

2 Roll the clay out on wax paper. Make it about 1/8–1/4 inch thick. (Larger pendants should be thicker.)

3 Use any type of object to cut out a shape in the clay.

4 Use a rubber or metal stamp to imprint a design in the clay.

5 Poke a hole for the cord with a chopstick. It needs to be wide enough to fit 2 strands of cord.

6 Allow to dry for 2–3 days.

7 Once dry, you can sand off the rough edges, paint, and finish making it into a jewelry item or a pendant diffuser.

INSTRUCTIONS:

1. Lay out a section of wax paper on a table to create your work station. This will help with cleanup and make it easier to roll out the clay and move the pieces.
2. Optional step: Take a glob of the clay, and color it using food coloring if desired. (Note: The clay always dries to be a lighter color.) (*Helpful hint: to make sure the food coloring stays in the clay and doesn't drip off, create a well in the top of the piece of clay with your finger, drop only 2 drops of coloring in the well at a time, fold the clay so it closes over the well opening, and then continue to knead the clay as normal. If it starts to feel dry, just add a few drops of water.)
3. Roll out the clay on the wax paper. You want it about 1/8–1/4 inch for pendants smaller than 1 1/4 inches. If you are creating larger pendant diffusers for a small room, you may want it to be thicker so it doesn't break as easily.
4. Use your cutout object to cut out the pendants. With the remaining clay, you can form beads by rolling it into small pieces and poking a hole through them with the chopstick or other stick.
5. Stamp your design on the pendants, and poke a hole through each of them for the cord with the chopstick or other stick.
6. Transfer pendants and beads to a paper plate, and allow them to air dry for 2–3 days.
7. Once dry, you can sand rough edges with sandpaper, decorate with paint, and/or finish making them into a piece of jewelry.
8. When figuring out the length of cord you will need, position the cord around the wrist or neck to the length you desire. Then cut double the length you think you will need. (You can always cut more off if it ends up being too long. We have found that adding any beads or knots takes up more string than you think it will.)
9. Put the ends together, creating a loop at the other end. String the pendant through the loop and the cut ends through the loop, securing the pendant in the middle before adding any beads.
10. If desired, a bead can be used to make a clasp for a necklace or bracelet by tying the bead to one side and making a loop big enough to go around the bead on the other side and securing it with a knot.
11. To use, simply place a drop of essential oil on the pendant, and rub the oil around. After a minute, the clay should have soaked up the oil and begun to diffuse. Reapply oil as the scent fades.

MAKE & TAKE CLASS IDEA: NATURAL CLEANING SPRAYS

Time: 30–45 minutes active; 24–72 hours inactive   Difficulty: Easy

When the weather turns warmer, you may be getting anxious to start your spring cleaning... or you may be dreading it. Either way, making all-natural cleaners can help you get started on the right foot! But rather than simply making the cleaners on your own, why not turn it into a make & take essential oil class!

FIGURE OUT HOW YOU WILL DO THE MAKE & TAKE WORKSHOP

There are a few different ways you can approach the workshop portion of the class. First, figure out which recipes you want to use, and then gather the necessary items. You can use any of the recipes in the cleaning section of this book (pages 186–201), the recipes found in the Kitchen and Bathroom Cleaning and Disinfecting section found in *Modern Essentials*, or any recipes of your own.

THE FOLLOWING ARE SOME IDEAS FOR DOING THIS MAKE & TAKE CLASS:

• Give away a cleaning spray to those who are new to essential oils or to those who sign up with you at your class.

• Charge per cleaning spray your attendees create. Just figure out the cost for all the items needed to make each spray, and let them make as many as they want and be charged accordingly. Make sure to include tax and shipping costs that you may have paid when figuring the cost. Do these calculations beforehand, and create a price sheet so you can easily reference it during the class. Offer a kit price. If you are offering a few different recipes for sprays, you may want to come up with a kit price that allows them to make one of all the different cleaning sprays.

• Figure out costs without oils. If you are doing this class as something fun for people who already use essential oils, you can have them bring their own oils or make the spray without the oils and have them add the oils later. This would reduce the cost for each spray, so you may want to calculate those costs beforehand.

• Charge only for the bottle. Since all of the ingredients are pretty inexpensive and can be used for a variety of purposes (or may even be items you already own), you may want to consider only charging for the glass spray bottle. When calculating the price, make sure to include any tax or shipping costs. If you do this, you can offer a flat price and let your students choose which cleaner they want to make or how many they want to make without the hassle of explaining the various prices.

NATURAL CLEANING SPRAYS

MAKE & TAKE CLASS IDEAS

YOUR CHOICE OF ESSENTIAL OIL

HOT CHOCOLATE SOCIAL

MAKE & TAKE CLASS IDEAS

PEPPERMINT ESSENTIAL OIL

PEPPERMINT HOT CHOCOLATE

Servings: 2   Time: 10 minutes active   Difficulty: Easy

INGREDIENTS:
- 2 1/2 Tbsp. unsweetened cocoa powder
- 1 1/2 Tbsp. sugar or other sweetener
- Pinch of salt
- 3/4 cup canned coconut milk (shake before opening)
- 1 1/2 cups milk (almond or rice milk work too)
- 1–2 drops peppermint essential oil

INSTRUCTIONS:
1. In a saucepan, mix together the cocoa powder, sugar, and salt.
2. Add coconut milk, and heat until combined.
3. Slowly add milk while continuing to stir. Keep stirring until little bubbles start to form on the surface.
4. Remove from heat. Allow to cool slightly. Stir in a drop or two of peppermint essential oil.
5. Pour into mugs, and serve. Warning: It will be hot, so allow the hot chocolate to cool to a reasonable temperature before drinking.
6. Top with whipped cream, marshmallows, chocolate chips, or ground peppermint candy.

Next time you need to plan an essential oil event, consider holding a hot chocolate social! This is a great idea for a team meeting or for a class to introduce new clients to essential oils.

Provide hot chocolate and various hot chocolate toppings, such as whipped cream, crushed candy cane, marshmallows, and chocolate chips. Also provide various essential oils to add to the hot chocolate. Peppermint, orange, and cassia essential oil all make great additions to hot chocolate. Instruct guests to just dip a toothpick in the oil and then swish the toothpick around in their hot chocolate.

Once everyone has helped themselves to hot chocolate and is sitting comfortably, this is a great time to share information about essential oils. You could focus on the health benefits of the oils you offered as hot chocolate mix-ins, provide basic introductory information about essential oils, discuss essential oils for winter wellness, or talk about cooking with essential oils.

Make sure that everyone is comfortable, enjoys some delicious hot chocolate, and has a really fun and positive experience! Be sure to send information about essential oils home with your guests so that they can continue to learn more about essential oils. It's also really great if you can send your guests home with a sample of essential oil to try out for themselves.

WINTER TIME PREP

MAKE & TAKE CLASS IDEAS

LAVENDER, EUCALYPTUS, ROSEMARY, & PEPPERMINT ESSENTIAL OILS

HAND CLEANSER

Yield: Two 4 oz. bottles or four 2 oz. bottles   Time: **20 minutes active**   Difficulty: **Easy**

INGREDIENTS:

- 1 cup aloe vera gel
- 1 Tbsp. witch hazel
- 30 drops (1/4 tsp.) melaleuca essential oil
- 10 drops lavender essential oil
- Clear oval plastic bottles with disc-top caps

INSTRUCTIONS:

1. In a small glass dish, add ingredients, and stir well.
2. Using a funnel, pour the hand cleanser mixture into the bottles.
3. Shake well before using.

BREATHE EASY SHOWER DISKS

Yield: 6   Time: **10 minutes active; 20 minutes inactive**   Difficulty: Easy

INGREDIENTS:

- 1 cup baking soda
- 1/3 cup water
- Eucalyptus essential oil
- Lavender essential oil
- Rosemary essential oil

INSTRUCTIONS:

1. Mix the baking soda and water together to form a paste. Add more water, if needed, to reach the desired consistency.
2. Prepare a muffin tin by adding cupcake liners. If you have a silicone muffin tin, you don't need the cupcake liners.
3. Pour the baking soda mixture into the cupcake liners (about 1/2 full).
4. Bake at 350 degrees Fahrenheit for 15–20 minutes, or leave on the counter to dry overnight.
5. Once baked, allow to cool completely before adding a couple drops of each of the essential oils on each disk. If you wish, you can add the oils right before you shower.
6. To use, simply place a disk on the floor of the shower, and allow the steam to diffuse the oils as you take a shower.

HOMEMADE CHEST & THROAT SALVE

Yield: **1/2 cup**   Time: **10 minutes active**   Difficulty: **Easy**

INGREDIENTS AND MATERIALS NEEDED:

- 1 1/2 Tbsp. beeswax pellets
- 6 Tbsp. coconut oil
- 1/2 tsp. arrowroot powder (optional: helps thicken the salve if stored in a warmer environment)
- 20 drops eucalyptus essential oil
- 20 drops peppermint essential oil
- Glass salve jar

INSTRUCTIONS:

1. Melt the beeswax and coconut oil in the microwave or on the stovetop in a pan filled with an inch of simmering water (creating a double boiler). Heat until completely melted.
2. Add arrowroot powder if desired.
3. Allow to cool for a minute before mixing in the essential oils.
4. Pour into the glass salve jar. Allow to cool completely before using.
5. To use, rub on chest, nose, and/or feet to support healthy respiratory system function.

TOP 4 TIPS TO SUPPORT HEALTHY IMMUNE SYSTEM FUNCTION DURING THE WINTER SEASON:

1. Get plenty of rest, and try to get as much sunshine as possible. If our bodies are well rested and have sufficient quantities of vitamin D, we can better protect against environmental and seasonal threats.

2. Get a water bottle that you can use with essential oils, and keep a small bottle of lemon or Protective Blend in your purse or backpack. Add 1–2 drops of oil to your water, and drink it throughout the day to help support healthy immune function.

3. Use a diffuser to diffuse essential oil throughout your home or office to purify the air.

4. Wash hands often, especially before meals or after coming home from public places. If you aren't able to wash your hands with soap and water, consider carrying a bottle of hand cleanser with you.

DIFFUSING BLENDS

CALMING SCENT

 +

5 drops lavender
essential oil

3 drops Roman
chamomile
essential oil

FLOWERS APLENTY

 +  +

3 drops lavender
essential oil

2 drops geranium
essential oil

1 drop Roman
chamomile
essential oil

ENERGIZING BLEND

 +  +

3 drops orange
essential oil

1 drop rosemary
essential oil

4 drops peppermint
essential oil

REFRESHING BLEND

 +  +  +

1 drop lavender
essential oil

1 drop rosemary
essential oil

1 drop melaleuca
essential Oil

1 drop peppermint
essential oil

DEEP BREATH

 +

3 drops peppermint
essential oil

3 drops eucalyptus
essential oil

RELAXING BREATH

 +

3 drops lavender
essential oil

3 drops bergamot
essential oil

CITRUS SPICE

 +  +  +

3 drops lemon
essential oil

4 drops orange
essential oil

2 drops grapefruit
essential oil

1 drop clove
essential oil

STRESS LESS

 +  +  +

2 drops lemon
essential oil

2 drops orange
essential oil

2 drops clove
essential oil

2 drops cedarwood
essential oil

SPRINGTIME BLISS

 +  +

| 1 drop ylang ylang essential oil | 2 drops lavender essential oil | 5 drops orange essential oil |

HOLIDAY GLOW

 +  +

| 3 drops cinnamon bark essential oil | 7 drops white fir essential oil | 5 drops orange essential oil |

WINTER WONDERLAND

 +  +

| 1 drop frankincense essential Oil | 2 drops orange essential oil | 1 drop peppermint essential oil |

APPENDIX

ESSENTIAL OILS & BLENDS QUICK USAGE CHART

ESSENTIAL OILS	COMMON USES
ARBORVITAE	Protects against environmental and seasonal threats. Promotes healthy cell function. Powerful cleansing and purifying agent. Natural insect repellent.
BASIL	Soothes sore muscles and joints. Assists with clear breathing. Acts as a cooling agent for the skin.
BERGAMOT	Reduces tension and stress. Promotes healthy, clear skin. Soothes and rejuvenates skin.
BIRCH	Soothes muscles and joints. Supports healthy circulation. Promotes clear breathing and healthy respiratory function. Beneficial for oily skin conditions. Stimulates the mind and enhances focus.
BLACK PEPPER	Rich source of antioxidants. Supports healthy circulation. Aids digestion. Enhances food flavor. Soothes nerves and lessens anxious feelings.

ESSENTIAL OILS & BLENDS QUICK USAGE CHART (CONTINUED)	
ESSENTIAL OILS	COMMON USES
CARDAMOM	◗ Eases occasional indigestion. ◗◒ Maintains an optimal gastrointestinal balance. ◒◒ Promotes clear breathing and respiratory health. ◗ Flavorful spice for cooking and baking. ◗◒ Calms occasional stomach upset and uplifts mood.
CASSIA	◗ Promotes healthy digestion. ◒ Supports healthy immune function. ◒ Warming, uplifting aroma. ◒ Helps soothe sore, achy joints.
CEDARWOOD	◒ Supports and maintains healthy respiratory function. ◒ Promotes clear, healthy skin. ◒◒ Evokes feelings of wellness and vitality. ◒ Relaxing, soothing aroma.
CILANTRO	◗ Aids digestion. ◗◒ Rich in antioxidants. ◗ Gives food a fresh and tasty flavor. ◒ Soothing to the skin.
CINNAMON	◒ Promotes circulation. ◒ Helps alleviate sore muscles and joints. ◒ Maintains a healthy immune system. ◗ Long used as natural flavoring and for its internal health benefits.

ESSENTIAL OILS & BLENDS QUICK USAGE CHART (CONTINUED)

ESSENTIAL OILS	COMMON USES
CLARY SAGE	Soothes monthly discomfort associated with menstrual cycles. Helps balance hormones. Soothes nervous tension and lightens mood. Calming and soothing to the skin.
CLOVE	Powerful antioxidant properties. Supports cardiovascular health. Promotes oral health and helps soothe teeth and gums.
CORIANDER	Promotes digestion and eases occasional stomach upset. Helps maintain an already healthy insulin response. Soothes joint and muscle discomfort. Tones and rejuvenates the skin. Helps oily skin areas to reduce breakouts.
CYPRESS	Assists with clear breathing. Promotes healthy respiratory function. Soothes tight, tense muscles. Supports localized blood flow. Beneficial for oily skin conditions.
EUCALYPTUS	Assists with clear breathing. Supports overall respiratory health. Soothes tired, sore muscles. Helps to lessen stress. Promotes oral health.

ESSENTIAL OILS	COMMON USES
FENNEL (SWEET)	⬤◐⬤Relieves occasional indigestion and digestive troubles. ⬤⬤Eases monthly menstrual cycles. ⬤Supports a healthy lymphatic system. ⬤Clams minor skin irritation.
FRANKINCENSE	⬤⬤Helps build and maintain a healthy immune system. ⬤⬤◐Promotes cellular health. ⬤Reduces the appearance of blemishes and rejuvenates skin. ⬤Promotes feelings of peace, relaxation, satisfaction, and overall wellness.
GERANIUM	⬤Promotes clear, healthy skin. ⬤⬤Helps calm nerves and lessen stress. ⬤⬤Supports liver health.
GINGER	◐⬤Helps ease occasional indigestion and nausea. ◐⬤Promotes digestion. ◐⬤Supports overall digestive health.
GRAPEFRUIT	⬤⬤◐Cleanses and purifies. ⬤Beneficial for oily skin issues. ⬤◐Supports healthy metabolism. ⬤⬤Helps reduce mental and physical fatigue. ⬤Helps with sore muscles and joints.

ESSENTIAL OILS	COMMON USES
HAWAIIAN SANDALWOOD	Promotes healthy, smooth skin. Reduces the appearance of scars and blemishes. Enhances mood. Frequently used in meditation for its grounding and uplifting properties.
HELICHRYSUM	Helps skin recover quickly. Promotes healthy liver function. Supports localized blood flow. Helps reduce the appearance of wrinkles and other blemishes. Helps relieve tension.
JASMINE	Evokes feelings of joy, peace, and self-confidence. Helps balance hormones and manage the symptoms of PMS. Promotes a healthy, glowing complexion. Nourishes and protects the skin and scalp.
JUNIPER BERRY	Supports healthy kidney and urinary function. May benefit problematic skin areas. Acts as a natural cleansing and detoxifying agent. Helps relieve tension and stress.
LAVENDER	Widely used for its calming and relaxing qualities. Soothes occasional skin irritations. Helps skin recover quickly. Eases muscle tension in the head and neck.

ESSENTIAL OILS & BLENDS QUICK USAGE CHART (CONTINUED)

ESSENTIAL OILS	COMMON USES
LEMON	Cleanses and purifies the air and surfaces. Naturally cleanses the body and aids in digestion. Supports healthy respiratory function. Promotes a positive mood and cognitive ability. Helps ward off free radicals with its antioxidant benefits. Soothes an irritated throat.
LEMONGRASS	Supports healthy digestion. Soothes aching muscles and joints. Purifies and tones skin. Heightens awareness and promotes a positive outlook.
LIME	Supports healthy immune function. Positively affects mood with stimulating and refreshing properties. Used as an aromatic, topical, and internal cleanser. Promotes emotional balance and well-being.
MARJORAM	Valued for its calming properties and positive effect on the nervous system. Soothes tired, stressed muscles. Supports a healthy respiratory system. Benefits the cardiovascular system.
MELALEUCA	Renowned for its cleansing and rejuvenating effects on the skin. Promotes healthy immune function. Protects against environmental and seasonal threats.

ESSENTIAL OILS & BLENDS QUICK USAGE CHART (CONTINUED)

ESSENTIAL OILS	COMMON USES
MELISSA	Supports and helps boost a healthy immune system. Calms tension and nerves. Addresses occasional stomach discomfort.
MYRRH	Powerful cleansing properties, especially for the mouth and throat. Soothing to the skin; promotes a smooth, youthful-looking complexion. Promotes emotional balance and well-being.
ORANGE	Powerful cleanser and purifying agent. Protects against environmental and seasonal threats. High in antioxidants. Uplifting to the mind and body.
OREGANO	Used as a powerful cleansing and purifying agent. Supports healthy digestion and respiratory function. Excellent source of antioxidants.
PATCHOULI	Grounding, balancing effect on emotions. Helps skin recover quickly. Soothes minor skin irritations. Helps with head and neck tension.

ESSENTIAL OILS & BLENDS QUICK USAGE CHART (CONTINUED)

ESSENTIAL OILS	COMMON USES
PEPPERMINT	Promotes healthy respiratory function and clear breathing. Alleviates occasional stomach upset. Frequently used in toothpaste and chewing gum for oral health.
ROMAN CHAMOMILE	Has a therapeutic, calming effect on the skin, mind, and body. Soothes the systems of the body. Supports healthy immune system function.
ROSE	Helps balance moisture levels in the skin. Reduces the appearance of skin imperfections. Promotes an even skin tone and healthy complexion. Emotionally uplifting.
ROSEMARY	Supports healthy digestion. Soothes sore muscles and joints. Helps reduce nervous tension and fatigue.
SANDALWOOD	Promotes healthy, smooth skin. Reduces the appearance of blemishes. Enhances mood. Frequently used in meditation for its grounding and uplifting properties.

ESSENTIAL OILS & BLENDS QUICK USAGE CHART (CONTINUED)

ESSENTIAL OILS	COMMON USES
THYME	Provides cleansing and purifying effects for the skin. Broad-spectrum activity in promoting winter-time health.
VETIVER	Supports healthy circulation. Calming, grounding effect on emotions. Immune-enhancing properties.
WHITE FIR	Provides soothing support to sore muscles and joints. Supports clear breathing and respiratory function. Energizes the body and the mind. Evokes feelings of stability, energy, and empowerment. Helps the body relax.
WINTERGREEN	Soothes achy muscles and joints. Promotes healthy respiratory function.
YLANG YLANG	Helps balance hormones. Promotes healthy skin and hair. Lifts mood while having a calming effect. Helps to lessen tension and stress. Promotes a positive outlook.

ESSENTIAL OILS & BLENDS QUICK USAGE CHART (CONTINUED)

ESSENTIAL OIL BLENDS	COMMON USES
ANTI-AGING BLEND	Reduces the appearance of fine lines and wrinkles. Helps reduce contributing factors to aging skin. Supports skin at a cellular level. Helps sustain smoother, more radiant, and youthful skin.
BLEND FOR WOMEN	Combines with each individual's chemistry to create a beautiful, unique, and personal fragrance. Provides a warming, musky aroma that entices the senses and intrigues the mind. Calms the skin and emotions.
CALMING BLEND	Calming, renewing fragrance. Promotes relaxation and restful sleep. Diffuses into a subtle aroma; ideal for aromatic benefits. Lessens tension and calms emotions. Helps reduce worry and stress.
CELLULAR COMPLEX	Supports healthy cellular integrity by helping to reduce oxidative stress. Supports healthy cellular function and metabolism. Protects the body and cells from oxidative stress.
CLEANSING BLEND	Refreshing aroma. Eradicates unpleasant odors and clears the air. Protects against environmental threats.

ESSENTIAL OILS & BLENDS QUICK USAGE CHART (CONTINUED)	
ESSENTIAL OIL BLENDS	COMMON USES
DETOXIFICATION BLEND	◐⊜Supports the body's natural ability to rid itself of unwanted substances. ◐⊜Supports healthy liver function. ◐⊜Purifying and detoxifying to the body's systems.
DIGESTIVE BLEND	◐⊜Aids in the digestion of foods. ◐⊜Soothes occasional stomach upset. ◐⊜Maintains a healthy gastrointestinal tract.
FOCUS BLEND	⊜⊘Enhances and sustains focus. ⊜⊘Supports efforts of those who have difficulty paying attention and staying on task. ⊘Promotes healthy thought processes.
GROUNDING BLEND	⊘⊜Creates a sense of calm and well-being. ⊘Promotes whole-body relaxation. ⊜Soothes sore muscles and joints. ⊜Promotes circulation. ⊜Supports cellular health and overall well-being. ⊘⊜Lessens stress and helps with anxious feelings and nerves.
HEADACHE RELIEF BLEND	⊜⊘Eases muscle tension in the head and neck. ⊜⊘Helps reduce tension, stress, and worry. ⊘Soothes the mind and body. ⊘Calms emotions.

ESSENTIAL OIL BLENDS	COMMON USES
INVIGORATING BLEND	Cleanses and purifies the air and surfaces. Helps reduce stress and uplift mood. Positively affects mood with energizing and refreshing properties.
JOYFUL BLEND	Elevates mood and increases vitality. Energizing, refreshing aroma. Helps to lessen sad and anxious feelings. Promotes a positive mood and energized mind and body.
MASSAGE BLEND	Relaxes muscles and soothes joints. Promotes circulation. Helps to calm and sooth target areas.
METABOLIC BLEND	Promotes healthy metabolism. Stimulates the endocrine system. Helps manage hunger cravings. Calms your stomach and lifts your mood. Promotes a positive mood. Helps purify and cleanses the body.
PROTECTIVE BLEND	Supports healthy immune function. Protects against environmental threats. Cleans surfaces. Purifies the skin while promoting healthy circulation. Energizing, uplifting aroma.

ESSENTIAL OILS & BLENDS QUICK USAGE CHART (CONTINUED)	
ESSENTIAL OIL BLENDS	COMMON USES
REPELLENT BLEND	Acts as an effective, natural repellent. Helps ward off insects.
RESPIRATORY BLEND	Maintains clear airways and breathing. Supports overall respiratory health. Helps minimize the effects of seasonal threats.
SOOTHING BLEND	Soothes sore muscles and achy joints. Supports healthy circulation.
TOPICAL BLEND	Helps keep skin clean, clear, and hydrated. Promotes clear, smooth skin. Soothes skin irritations. Assists in cell renewal.
WOMEN'S MONTHLY BLEND	Helps balance hormones. Provides temporary respite from cramps, hot flashes, and emotional swings.

BUNNY BUDDY
PATTERN

INDEX